TOUCH
THE OCEAN

*The Power of Our
Collective Emotions*

BY

James Nemec, LMT, CST-D

CraniOcean Media

TOUCH THE OCEAN
The Power of Our Collective Emotions

Copyright © 2007 by James Nemec

Published by
CraniOcean Media
West Palm Beach, Florida

Orders at *Info@RazorPages.com*
http://www.CraniOcean.com

Cover Design by George Foster • Book Design by William Groetzinger

Edition ISBN
Softcover   978-0-9792805-0-4

Published in the United States of America
First Edition 2007.

Publisher's Cataloging-in-Publication
(Provided by Quality Books, Inc.)

Nemec, James.
    Touch the ocean : the power of our collective
emotions / by James Nemec.
    p. cm.
    Includes bibliographical references.
    ISBN-13: 9780979280504
    ISBN-10: 0979280508

    1. Craniosacral therapy. 2. Emotions. 3. Human
ecology. 4. Healing. 5. Mind and body. I. Title.

RZ399.C73N46 2007   615.8'2
                                     QBI07-600027

DEDICATION

To Mom and Dad and the House
and all Poets everywhere,
including all Dolphins,
and to Playwright J. Allen Boone,
who wrote *Kinship With All Life*,
after finding himself
in a similar situation,
and thus dedicated to All Life.

Deep in the sea are riches beyond compare.
But if you seek safety, it is on the shore.

Saadi

...They walked over meadows, fields, and stones the
entire day, and when it began to rain, the sister said,
'God and our hearts are weeping at the same time.'

Grimm's Fairy Tale, "Brother and Sister"

TOUCH THE OCEAN

INTRODUCTION

All it may take to touch the ocean is the simple feeling of being in gratitude.

We know less about the depths of our oceans than we do about the known universe, much less the mysteries of the human brain. Our bodies are for the most part, oceans in miniature, made of seventy-eighty percent water, but this water is not always happy and in flow. Like the polluted land masses of our planet, there are places within where our water is stagnant, tainted, unhappy. I am not introducing a theory or making a self help manual. I am only suggesting we can find out for ourselves in our own experience for the answer is within our hands and our very feelings. No one need read a book, stop smoking, meditate, go to the gym, do yoga, take a course, take on a relationship, get a divorce, or make a million dollars to find out, the answer is here, in your hands.

All it takes is a very light touch.

There is a way of doing things to the ocean, and a way of being with the ocean, the sky, even the weather in our quiet moments, wherever we may be located geographically. Within the waters of our bodies are held stories, dramas, comedies; stories our bodies can tell. Some of these stories are nurturing and nourishing to the whole body, to ourselves, and to others, and yet other stories are not. Some of our bodies' waters may be shark infested and dark, others flow with whales and dolphins and delicate changes of light. What waters do we choose to live in?

The choice is our own if we care to look within and find out. Some of our bodies' stories are of chronic tension patterns, chaos, disorder, disintegration, and of resistance to change. Others are of harmonious patterns, flow, and openness to change, health, and new life. To find out, rather than make up new stories, or rather than dump good water into bad water, we might take time to look at the stories already here in our waters and running not only the show, but the flow of our lives. If we can only take this time, we might possibly discover the stories that block us from our God given flow in living and being alive.

This is not to judge the waters of any ocean.

As a playwright, I took time out from writing my plays to write *Touch the Ocean* because I found the discoveries of some value to health and to the healing of ourselves, others, even the ocean, which is as hated as it is loved, and felt the nonfiction form was the most appropriate way to show what is possible. If only one facet of information is discovered and used for one person's benefit on the planet now, it makes this effort worthwhile. And as a healing artist, I have routinely preferred to work one-on-one with those who have known little to nothing of "me" or of "my" background or art, and yet who am I to withhold useful information from this or future generations now? This storybook may possibly disturb some of the clients and patients I have had the immeasurable privilege to work with over the years, and who have known of "me" only through a veil. Yet others have known only the internet name, "CraniOcean."

This book is a distillation, an elixir, of a much larger work of actual case histories written when first opening to the miracles of Healing. *Touch the Ocean* now becomes the first book in a continuing series of showing what's possible, and will be followed by *Journeys: Stories Our Bodies Can Tell, Awake and Asleep: Stories Our Bodies Can Tell,* and finally, a total and delightful surprise! For ease of reading and narrative flow, I have compressed twelve years of events into a period of about two weeks. The events you are about to read are very personal to myself and to others and concern our intimate mutual growth. I would like to thank each person for the vast privilege of letting their stories be told, and I would also like to thank the dolphins, Trinidad and Tobago.

Parts One and Two of *Touch the Ocean* are about how, after three years of working at an acute care clinic in Los Angeles without formal training as a massage therapist, I encountered a healing art which I could hardly pronounce, "Craniosacral Therapy," after having been led to it through a series of circumstances beyond my control. Parts Three and Four are about how I began to use this healing art in the exploration of work with dolphins in the Bahamas and then with the ocean off Palm Beach, Florida. All of the conversations and events in *Touch the Ocean* are true, some of the names are real and some have been changed, and all occurred in the same geographical locations as mentioned in the book, just over a greater span of time.

The book poses this question, "Can one light touch change the world?" One can only find out about this for oneself. I'm following my own fascination. And I'm still making discoveries, thankfully. A friend asked me how I felt after I'd written this book, and I said, "I know less now than I did before." This book is as much about not knowing as it is about knowing. Again and again it opens to our sense of mystery and enchantment. The questions the flowing and flowering narrative asks are part of the total contemplation that is *Touch the Ocean* and of the author's own.

What is it to sit with a question without having to have an immediate answer?

Touch the Ocean is about a way of being with ourselves and others, being with the ocean and the sky in a healing context, even with the weather and weather patterns. It is also about a new way of light touch, largely unknown, which is proven to relieve and treat an array of symptoms from migraines to depression, scoliosis to seizures, autism to asthma, TMJ to ADD, and above all, which gently helps us to discover old story patterns long held within our bodies and to harmlessly release them. *Touch the Ocean* shows us that once old and cumbersome stories are discovered in our oceanic bodies, space opens within our body, mind, spirit, to let new water enter in and new life. We will also learn how it's the small influences, the light touch, that can matter the most as we move into the story waters of the dolphins, the ocean, and of our oceans within. The flowing narrative of this book, like the two healing sessions performed in the ocean itself, tends to flow much like a spiral moving into wider and wider arcs. (The center of the spiral is a rather surprising kiss!) Along the way, we will investigate a most extraordinary question: just as weather can affect our moods, can we influence the moods of the weather? When I casually mention this to people at parties or in my day job, the response is invariably, "Yes, like duh." Except for the occasional Blog on the Internet, there have been no real studies made to this date, that I know of, and no debates, yet if this is true, it can be of utmost concern in an increasingly interdependent global economy. If our collective actions and reactions can possibly influence the weather, then what are we doing to ourselves and to others, not to mention our pocketbooks? And possibly, if we are fortunate, we may learn how to learn to touch the ocean for ourselves. Sadly, the ocean is filled with more floating debris of civilization in the twenty-first century than it can tolerate and perhaps it now calls to us to explore the depths of our own oceans while there's time.

It was a crappy day and overcast. I went for a swim and there was too much Sargasso seaweed to move my arms. The sick brown seaweed was getting in my hair and under my legs and ankles. Mixed in the seaweed were plastic bottles and debris with alien bacterium and parasites that had traveled north through the Gulf Stream from the lower Caribbean Islands and South America. I stopped trying to swim. I pulled one bottle out, then another, I pulled and pulled. It was as if the ocean was puking it up. I'd never felt that feeling before when inside of her. I kept pulling and it was as if she kept puking. I took two full arm loads of the stuff across the beach and up to the thick plastic waste basket by the road. And I thought if one person could take away only one plastic bottle each time they visited the ocean it would be a different world.

It can take enormous attention and intention to not judge the ocean on such days, and rather, to see what can be done.

I'm not writing as an environmentalist. My day job is to work with the inner environment, the inner pollution. The outer pollution will never stop until we address the inner pollution. Taking care of both are random acts of consideration and a kindness to us all. It can take hundreds of years for the ocean to break down a single plastic grocery bag, seconds to pick up one plastic bottle from the beach, a moment for the direction of a life to change, for better or worse. I'm pointing to what is to our advantage to do, what is life affirming, what is life sustaining, not to another dreary course of self improvement or even of land management.

We are as wild as the ocean, as unpredictable, and in potential, as loving.

What does the ocean grudge the sky?

Will you join us on this journey? I consider each reader a guest on a visit to the story waters of this book, and I will do what I can to make your visit pleasant and comfortable, even humorous, for if nothing else, ocean, sky, even the weather can have a sense of humor! Of course, let us never forget the Source that animates all and the ALL, each moment, by whatever name most comfortable for you, God, the Infinite, Life, Love. Thank you for your time and travel to these waters and for making space to receive these words and feelings in these odd times-out-of-joint. And now, for our Prologue, a visit to the waters of a different ocean for who am I to tell others' stories without first including my own and yes, with its own floating debris.

Thank you.

J. Nemec
Los Angeles
November 2004

I

Soft Systems

PROLOGUE

I dreamed I saw Jack Kerouac. He wasn't alone. Allen Ginsberg was with him. In fact, I think it was Allen who showed up first. The dream image I'd had of him in his tweed coat and tie morphed into a wild image of him in the Chicago Conspiracy Trial outfit he wore in the Sixties complete with American Star Spangled Banner hat. His hair was psychedelic and his eyes swirled in red, white, and blue. Then the previous image of him morphed back into focus, the image in his Ivy League tweed in the days before his passing.

Once, Allen Ginsberg kissed me full on the mouth. I didn't know what was going on. I didn't know if I should wipe my mouth. The kiss happened in the hallway of a Tibetan Buddhist monastery in Vermont. I was the only person he kissed I knew of. I had been in deep meditation for weeks and was worried that meditation would destroy my ability to write and be creative when Allen showed up by surprise. He was there for a weekend. I was so excited, I played hooky from the meditation periods and wrote poetry and said hi to him every chance. He was there to do prostrations to the Buddha. On his second night there, I sat down with him in the cafeteria. No one else would sit with him. My fellow meditators weren't impressed with him because they felt he didn't meditate enough. He had done something like thirty-five thousand prostrations to the Buddha and they said he should do something like, say, one hundred and fifty thousand prostrations to the Buddha. I said back to them, "Man, his life is a meditation. He's Allen Ginsberg." This one woman rolled her eyes.

I'd asked Allen if a poet could write and meditate at the

same time.

"Sure."

I asked him about Jack Kerouac. He said, "Jack would just scribble. We'd be in a room upstairs talking and he'd sit off alone and scribble. He'd sit there hours."

"Cool. You mean, he'd write?"

It was snowing outside. The food wasn't much. I didn't feel up to the conversation and was grateful to keep him company. He looked at me. He had round eyes and a wide mouth.

"I'm convinced I'm Jesus Christ. I've thought about it for a long time and now I know."

"That's really something...."

"I'M JESUS CHRIST!"

"Wow."

I had no idea what he meant. I glanced around at the other tables. He didn't care who heard.

When I heard he was about to take off, I raced to the front hall and showed him one of my poems. It was just on the back of a plane ticket. He looked at it and said, "It's good, good. Just keep scribblin'."

"Scribblin'?"

"That's all Jack did."

Then the kiss.

This was the second time I'd been anywhere near Allen Ginsberg. The first time was when I was with my Dad. Six months before, my Dad and I were at this same monastery to see the cremation ceremony of a high, Tibetan Lama, the venerable Chogyam Trungpa Rinpoche. I loved Trungpa because he was a crazy wisdom master and spiritual madman and this gave me great joy.

Dad and I used to take father and son trips when I was little. We were part of the YMCA Indian Guides program and our motto was: Father and Son, Pals Forever. We'd also go duck hunting and stay at a cabin in Lake Okeechobee and shoot skeet. Dad thought we were going to take a trip to go backpacking in Vermont with llamas. He thought this because he'd seen a newspaper article in the Palm Beach Post Times about how people were backpacking with llamas in the woods of Vermont. He sent me the news article and it had a photo of furry white llamas. He'd scribbled, "Why not?" I laughed. I was interested in serious meditation and sudden enlightenment.

Why not?

My Tibetan Buddhist days followed my Native American Indian days which followed my Zen days which followed my Robert Bly and the Circle of Men and Drum Circle days. They followed my Shamanism days which followed my other Native American Indian days which followed my Hindu days which followed my Carlos Castaneda and Don Juan and the Yaqui Indian Way days. These were followed by my Macrobiotic days which followed my Taoist Healing days which followed my other Macrobiotic Days which followed my I-Ching and Tarot Divination days which followed my Existential Philosophy Day which followed my Transcendental Meditation days which followed my Pentecostal Christian and the Laying-on-Hands days which followed my Fundamentalist Christian Days which followed my plain old Southern Baptist Days which followed my surfer days. I enjoyed my surfer days. The surf is still good out in front of the house I grew up in, and I could check out the waves from my bedroom window with the bright sun blast of dawn in my face which made me rub sunscreen on my nose before bed, but after awhile, it was just wave after crystal blue wave, the same thing all over again, it felt too much like my life, an Endless Summer of the same thing over and over again and what was it all about, really? For what purpose?

It was the same thing at the First Baptist Church, over and over again, rededicating my life to the Lord, walking down the aisle. I could never resist the preacher when he said, "Won't you stand up for Jesus, just as you are, and walk down this aisle?" I had to sit on my hands in the pew so I wouldn't get up and go running to the

Baptismal fount.

After I called him up from Los Angeles and said, "No, Dad, it's not llamas. It's Lamas."

"What? Llamas?"

"Not llamas, but Lamas. It's a Tibetan Lama. They're going to cremate him."

He said, "Cremate a Lama?"

"Yeah, like with the ocher yellow robes? Buddhist guy."

"Oh, Buddhist? They're going to burn him up? This guy?"

"Yeah."

"Good! I want to see that! That would be good to see! Educational."

"But it's not backpacking," I said. "Okay?"

"Fine. I'll take the camera."

I didn't know then that my Dad would one day treat me to a trip to Macchu Picchu where we would see real llamas together.

We met at the small airport in Burlington, checked into a bed and breakfast, and then went to a meadow which held a huge, white plaster structure for the cremation ceremony. It was about fifty feet high and there were colorful, Tibetan prayer flags all around it. It was called a "stupa," a religious structure in which they burn the bodies of Lamas. Dad asked me to pose for the camera in front of the stupa, and when I looked up and smiled, I saw this guy in a dark suit with glasses and a beard who looked very similar to Allen Ginsberg. I said to myself, "It has to be."

"Come on, Dad, let's go meet this guy." Dad put the camera on pause. We went over a small rise in the meadow and I walked up and introduced myself. I said, "Jim Nemec, and this is my Dad, Jim Nemec. And you are?"

"Just call me Allen."

I said, "Cool. We're here for the ceremony."

He said, "Great." He excused himself to hang out with a poet from Peru.

"Dad," I said, "That was Allen Ginsberg."
"Who?"
I whispered. "Allen. He's a Poet."
"Buddhist fellow?"
"Yeah. Famous, too."
Dad focused his video on Allen and the poet from Peru.

M*y head turned, as if by itself, on my pillow. I couldn't place where I was. It was about this time Jack arrived. He came out of the shadows. He was quiet, distant.*
I said, "Jack? Are you all right?"
Nothing.
This was too much.
I felt hurt by Jack Kerouac for that whole year. I'd found out from a video I'd rented about him and his mother that they drank together and that the drink killed Jack in his home with his mother in the mountains of Massachusetts Berks — birth-O — all closed down and far from the home of The Railroad Earth. This was long after On The Road *and* The Dharma Bums *and* Mexico City Blues *and I never knew anything about it. I had been pissed because the two dollar and fifty cent video said he'd spent the rest of his life cloistered with his mother in his mother's home in the Berkshire Mountains and they drank each other to the death. He'd wasted his talent. But in fact, he died in Florida at the tender age of forty seven.*
Allen said, "You are about to write a book."
"Oh, yeah? What's it about?"
He said, "Health. On Healing." And he sparkled and a light started to grow around Jack.
"Wow!" Then I doubted. "Okay, I guess. But I write plays. I'm more a poet."

Things began to blur. I began to lose their images or they were losing me. It was like they were sparkling away into the dream-vision mist, but I had a sense in the way back of my mind that a conversation was still going on and to listen.

So I said to Jack, "You still write poetry where you are now?"

Allen looked to Jack, and then Jack said, "Man, I AM POETRY."

I could hear myself say, "Cooool."

Their images divided into moving vertical lines and then somehow re-solidified. And someone said, maybe both of them, I don't know, "It can happen with you, too. Book. Plays. Poems. We're here to tell you. If you'd like that."

It felt good. "Yeah." Then, "I don't know. The demons don't want me to write."

"We're here to tell you."

"Thank you. What are you guys now? Poets?"

Jack said, "Bodhisattvas."

And Allen said, "Bodhisattvas."

"So what do you do?" I asked.

Jack said: "We do what Bodhisattvas do."

Allen had this big smile.

There they stood in my dream not four feet away from the side of my queen sized bed. Jack Kerouac and Allen Ginsberg, the Bodhisattvas. It was way too much. I wanted to hate Jack Kerouac forever and his mother, but couldn't. And I wanted to hate my own mother, but she wasn't part of the dream. She'd died in Florida, too.

Jack said, "You stay on your purpose. That will see you through."

What was my purpose?

Then I said, "Jack? What about your mother? Where's she?"

There was a wave of shadows like shadow curtains. Jack's mother appeared in the background for a moment. She didn't look ravaged and dry in the face like I would have thought she would. She smiled.

I couldn't see her anymore. She'd disappeared. No chance she would ever say hi or hello to my mother. I wished she would. But they didn't know each other and my mother never drank. My mother wouldn't have liked her, not really, not in a million years.

Not long after I had broken free of Palm Beach to land in La La Land, my parents came to visit for Christmas and checked in at the Beverly Hills Hotel on Sunset. They had brought a Santa hat for me and a small pewter duck with brass wings. Mom asked me to get into my red Christmas pajamas from home so they could take a picture of me by the fake gold cellophane Christmas tree in their hotel room. I put on the hat and held the duck. It was a flash camera. I didn't smile. Then I went off to my job as waiter at an Italian restaurant on La Brea. I wasn't very good at being a waiter and was fired after my third shift. I'd dropped a full pitcher of beer at the restaurant owner's table at the Christmas party. It had shattered on the floor. After that, Mom asked me if I was happy that they had come to L.A. I said I wasn't and wished they'd go back to Florida. She said, "I'm sorry to hear that. And I'm sorry we came." "It's just I'm trying to be free and independent, Mom. It's hard with you and Dad around. I mean, you're at the Beverly Hills Hotel!" "You can make contacts in the show business here." "Oh, Mom!" Years later, I became tormented: maybe she was right. I knew I was a creature more acted upon than acting and there was nothing I could do about it. Now, I wondered if Jack Kerouac's mom ever left him alone? Why did he get off the road and go back home?

Jack said, "Stay on your purpose. Let all things be made new."

I knew what he meant deep down in my being. Allen started to speak, but I don't remember what he said. His voice was full of rhythm and music and just went on. I felt my hand twitch and my fingers move. My head rolled and I nestled back into the edges of my dream. I caught it just right and fell back into deep sleep with a question. They were still there.

"Stay on your new purpose."

Then from Jack's heart center I saw the shimmer of a golden, shining, many-armed Goddess Bodhisattva arise with Avalokiteshvara grace. Jack's face and body fell away and next to him I saw appear another light arising in Bodhisattva joy with spontaneous arm and finger mudras of peace. This was Ginsberg. It was as if a great light had stepped inside my room. I felt reassured about everything in that moment. They were okay.

Moments later, my head turned on the dank motel pillow. I caught a glimpse of green neon through the thin curtains. I had stopped the night near the Mojave Desert on my way back to L.A. and thought I was at home in my bedroom in Florida. When I wake up I wake up gradually. There is no forcing it. And there is no choosing it. And I awake.

DAD'S HEART BREAK

My journal says that today the nurse visited Dad at his office over on Palm Beach Lakes Boulevard and asked if he'd had any operations? He said he'd had a hysterectomy in Iran. Hysterectomy? It was during the War. They were making shipments of ammunition to the allies but their coolies were smuggling out bullets that they hid in their turbans. No one would go down into the hold of his Cargo ship. He was the Commander and it was up to him. He went down the ladder first and said to his men, "Follow me." It was dark in the belly of the hold. They couldn't use lights because of the gunpowder. And he could just see the coolies in their turbans hidden behind the barrels. He was the first to engage in hand to hand combat and after fierce fighting in darkness, all the smugglers were seized. It was nothing to smile at. He pointed out he had a citation for bravery, but the plaque wasn't here at the office. It was at the house over in Palm Beach.

The nurse listened. "No, you had a herniaectomy," she corrected.

"Yeah?"

She spelled it out. "Hernia-ectomy." She'd said she was here to check his medications. But she wouldn't be here consistently since the medications he was taking required that the person be homebound and Dad was too active for that.

"Thank goodness," he said.

Dad had been at Good Samaritan Hospital on Flagler Drive

in West Palm for a long time for a "tune up," as his doctor described it. Since Mom had passed, his mitral valve wasn't getting
closed enough by the suspensory ligament down below it, a touch
of mitral valve prolapse. And it had been flapping back open into
the atrium throwing blood.

I stepped out of his office and went to be alone in his law
library. What could I do? I'd done a session piece with him some
months before around his mitral valve at the house, days before
I had to go back to California. We were in the far end of the
Florida room, a room with a spray sparked ceiling that glinted
even in the twilight. He was in his pajamas with his feet up on
his big blue easy chair, and when he looked at me, his eyes looked
blue as the ocean.

Dad was a true blue Navy man and had bought the main
house from a sea captain in the early 1950's. It stands four stories high with a gabled red tile roof and white stucco walls. It sits
across the road from the ocean and always has the American flag
out front and is a landmark for the residents of the north end. It's
the highest house on that point of the island and still serves as a
guide at night to the pilot boats navigating the big ships into the
Palm Beach Inlet. My bedroom is just above Dad's room and is
under where the roof peaks into the last gable and is the highest
room in the house. No hurricane of any category has ever
knocked my bedroom windows down and inside it has the look
of rich, finished wood and angled white plaster walls like Ernest
Hemingway's house in Bimini.

Dad had built the Florida room as an addition to the main
house to accommodate large parties and everyone from church
families to John D. MacArthur of Insurance fame and his dear
friend, diva Helen Hayes, to the godforsaken winos of West Palm
Beach that Mom had taken pity on had all been invited to our
huge and roaring Thanksgiving dinners here for years, Thanks-

givings always blessed by the then pastor of the First Baptist Church of West Palm Beach, Jess C. Moody, and always amen'd! by his wife and son and daughter. We'd lay out long wood tables here in the Florida room and my sisters would decorate them with horns of plenty and sing Gershwin-like songs together that my Mom wrote for Dad after they married, just at the start of World War II. American families sang then. Every year there was the "Bing Crosby Christmas Special" with his family, the *Sound of Music* with the Von Trapp Family singers, and families singing in our church every Wednesday and Sunday nights. My sisters sang more than Dad and I outside of church. As a group, I'd call my sisters the Sisters of Mercy, even though we were not Catholic, and growing up, I'd go through the upstairs rooms of the house and manage to discover yet another sister doing something or other like reading. Each sister was like a new fish in the aquarium of my unformed mind. I got lost in the mix and after many years I realized I was raised a virgin to marry a rich white man.

The sound of the ocean and gentle breeze through the long rows of windows somehow supported Dad and I now. The Panasonic big screen TV, which stood sentinel by the sliding glass doors that opened to the south patio, was off. Soon after my hands were laid ever so gently over his forehead, he said, "Momma's here." This used to bother me a lot when he'd say this but I began to understand it was a blessing, if only because he misses her so darn much. It's always as if Mamma appears during sessions with Dad, even during our massage therapy sessions so long ago, not just in the Florida room but anywhere we'd set up to work. And she always appears in her sparkling white and gold banded gown that she wore for their 50th wedding anniversary at the Royal Poinciana Chapel on Coconut Row, her hair all up and silvery and highlighted with touches of deep black recalling her days in New York when she had her own radio show and was quite a looker. I knew her eyes were blue as Dad's but I've never seen her eyes like Dad does during sessions, only the feeling of the warmth of her smile.

Mom and Dad met during a dance at Stetson University in Deland, Florida. She was a Florida native, and he was born in Chicago on Harrison Street. He was there at the university on a football scholarship. Once he broke his leg and couldn't play and was taken off his scholarship and had to eat sandwiches that his teammates would sneak from the cafeteria to his attic apartment for almost a year. Once his leg recovered, he could play again and attend classes. I guess it was like that in those days. After they married, war broke out and he was transferred to New York where he worked at the Navy Yard in Brooklyn until his assignment to the Cargo ship. It was a match made in heaven.

Mom was here.

My hand moved to his heart and rested ever so gently there.

"What's your heart have to say about that? Anything?"

"I can feel you right here with me. But I miss you." He was talking to her.

"Does she have anything to say?" I ventured.

He listened. Then his head made a slight roll to one side. "She says, 'She's here.'"

Soft tears formed at the edges of his thick eyelids. The weak valve in heart began to glisten with a sparkling liquid light.

I said only, "Could it be possible for her to be with you this way now?"

His head rolled again on the easy chair, almost imperceptibly, and a liquid light seemed to open in his other valve. There was silence.

"I've been heartbroken. My heart," he said.

The two lights joined and a feeling of warmth and energy coursed through his whole body. There were no more words. When my hands finally came off his head and chest, as if by themselves, he looked at me with surprise mixed with gratitude.

He'd been heartbroken, astonishing. His heart knew, I thought. How 'bout that?

"That really helped. I can feel my heart. Thank you," he said.

I was surprised. It all happened in a matter of a few minutes.

"Thank you," I said. "But I didn't do it. You did it." After that, I was back in California.

He felt great for months.

Now, my hands felt the worn red leather in the chair in his library and I wondered about saying something to the nurse. She looked so out of context in her crisp white uniform and with her oxygen tank on wheels at the office. There's his heart doctors, radiologists, dermatologists, surgeons standing by. I couldn't keep up with them all. I was back from California now and had tried to talk to one of his heart doctors on a visit with Dad to Good Sam, but what could any of them do? The doctors had expected him to go after his first episode, months ago. And they were required to keep the medications going no matter how active he was and it seemed endless, oxytocin, cumadin, lasex, vitamins. I don't know if anyone in the family can still keep up with all his many different medications from his many different doctors. He needs a social director just for that. Then a dark thought: Everybody's on their own personal agenda.

What Dad could use is a lot less help. Why couldn't they just let him be? Let him heal? Not that I have anything at all against his doctors or his heart medications which are critically measured. But the drug companies had never met my Dad. They didn't know who he was or his strength. Had anyone working for those companies ever tried one of those medications on their own precious bodies? What about his doctors? I'd tried to speak to them about it but the words didn't come out right and I became quiet. It's hard to speak up in a hospital with all those white coats, machines, and smells. What would a story about his heart having been broken matter to anyone, much less a story told by his heart? Look, it's just heartbreak, that's all, give him more room to let the grief heal. Give him space. He may not know about it but his body knows, his body remembers. It would only have sounded like an interesting anecdote. His medications had been doubled since I'd been away and he'd asked if they could slow down on them. He said he felt better without them and had a lot to do. But in response, his social engagements were to be cut in half and to a man like my Dad it hurts to be told that.

What are some of his social engagements? The Pundits Club, the Pen Women of America where he is a "penguin," the Kiwanis Club, Palm Beach Round Table, Heart Ball, the upcoming Salvation Army Ball. He doesn't dance so much nowadays, not like he used to when we'd take the family to the large and opulent charity balls at the Breakers Hotel which, like the house, fronts the ocean. He taught me to dance with Mom first, then every one of the sisters and each elderly woman at our table. My sisters and I learned to respect our elders early on, especially those who couldn't dance very well. The balls are held in what's called, the Season. The Season lasts from late December to early March, depending on who you speak to. We grew up with The Season and going to the Balls, and since I had six sisters, Mom started the Debutante Ball, also held at the Breakers. I'd gone to cotillion as a kid and grew up with all the dance moves and would attend as an Escort or as a Stag, which is another word for single guy and dance with the Debutantes or "Debs" after they'd been promenaded around the grand hall by their fathers and given away to Society. Dad gave away his six daughters to Society but the Debutante Ball vanished from Palm Beach after my mother passed. Maybe he kept it in business. He says he goes to most the balls now but he'll be sitting a lot.

Who was the nurse? What could I say to her? She was just one kind person in a huge system to help my Dad.

I watched her collect her things to depart. Maybe I needed to ask her about me instead of Dad. Dad is so healthy now, I was thinking, what will my health be like in twenty five or forty years with my smoking and not exercising so much? Dad never smoked or had a drink in his life, at least, not around us kids when we were growing up. Mom didn't either.

Mom had been raised by a Baptist Minister and very disciplined mother out in Felsmere and the wetlands around Okeechobee and her parents had a lot to do with establishing the first Baptist churches around here. The family came to the big city of West Palm Beach on the ice boats that made regular stops along the canals. I couldn't recall how many children were in her family but most of them died young from swamp disease or accident. Dad was raised in Chicago and both his parents had immigrated from Prague, Czech Republic. His mother was wise yet practical and encouraged him to learn English by reading books, and his Dad made bathtub beer during prohibition and was a bouncer who packed a six shooter along Harrison Street, wherever that was. Dad's first job as a boy was to help deliver ice on a horse drawn wagon, then as a laborer in roof repair for twenty-five cents a week. But no one in their families had come up the ladder as far as Palm Beach and with six mostly healthy children. Dad started from nothing and had been praised in this part of the world as a self-made man, a card carrying member of the Great Generation.

This is opposed to the Wrecked Generation of which his

proud grandchildren would become a part, the generation of
drug and alcohol abuse and traffic fatalities that is current now,
a generation out of answers and short on health alternatives despite the number of churches and schools and drugs available to
them. I wondered what "generation" I was a part of. I was born
just after the Hippie Generation and wasn't Generation X or Y.
Maybe I was the Sting Generation following The Police, or the
Smoking is Okay generation. I'd take a cigarette any day of the
week to any one of his doctors' prescriptions, or this nurse's.
Probably best to do neither, who knows? But comfort for a man
his age has to count for something.

"You ready, Dad?"

He handed a deposition to his secretary, Helen, and looked
at me, a blank.

We'd talked about this before but I'd review him on it. "There's
you and there's me and there's the space in between us," I enthused. "It's invisible. And what's in that space? It's where we
connect together. It's our relationship. And that's what we're going to work on. Okay?"

The nurse listened without comprehension. Helen smiled.
Helen knew how much this moment meant to him, to both of us.

"I'm all for it," he said.

"Let's go!"

He reached and we shook hands and he made a guttural noise
like a grizzly bear on an Alaskan salmon. He grabbed his gray silk
coat and put his favorite Navy cap around his head. It was given
to him by the Navy when he was invited to tour the USS Ala-
bama for a weekend, a Trident class nuclear powered submarine.
My second oldest sister, Ruthie, entered the office in a rush
through the sculpted wooden door. On the lapel of her *Century
21* blazer she wore one of the colorful butterfly brooches that
she'd made by hand for all of us before Mom's funeral. Mom was

a butterfly, she'd said, and her Spirit would fly up to the sky. She'd been handling the details of Dad's estate and had pressing questions. She turned around and followed Dad out to the hall. "It can wait," he said.

"FATHER AND SON, PALS FOREVER"

We turned onto I-95 in his Cadillac and headed north to Palm Beach Gardens. Large dark clouds had gathered and were full with rain, but there were only slight sprinkles, and there was no need to turn on the windshield wipers. The black car had been hot as an oven and I hoped it would rain some just to help out the air conditioner, but then there would be the sticky feeling of humidity mixed with the heat of the summer. The exit was PGA Boulevard, the same exit that Dad had taken to his golf club as long as I could remember.

"Maybe we'll go to Ballen Isles after," he said.

Ballen Isles used to be called JDM, for John D. MacArthur. "Sure."

I hadn't been to Dad's golf club in years and only then for social occasions, birthdays with the family. I remembered when I was a surfer in my teens and how hard it was for Dad to teach me golf. Each tee off led into an argument: I could never do it right.

"Remember when we would play golf, Dad?"

"We only did that once or twice."

"I've gotten pretty good at hitting the ball out on the driving range."

"Yeah, you can hit a ball now, but it took a lot."

I paid attention to the driving. Whenever I drive the black Cadillac it's as if the car floats to either side of the road. Maybe it has to do with the alignment.

"Here," said Dad, and motioned with his hand toward the exit.

The Healthplex Clinic was on Prosperity Farms Road and a newcomer to the area. It used to be woods and swamp and Dad and I would trek out here on father and son trips with the YMCA. We were part of the Indian Guides, a youth group that would show us the traditional ways of the North American Native Indians, as best as anyone could guess. We would make moccasins and learn songs and had our own Indian names, like Geronimo and Sitting Bull.

Once we went out to Lake Placid for a weekend powwow and stayed in Indian Lodges and a few of us fathers and sons took a canoe trip across the lake to look at the nice cows over there but there were bulls with the cows and they got scared and stampeded and Dad got into the middle of the herd with a pine branch and whooped and hollered and split the herd and turned the stampede away from us kids so we could escape back to the canoes under barbed wire fences. He was heartily congratulated and thanked by all. The motto on our T-shirts said, Father and Son, Pals Forever.

"Remember the Indian Guides, Dad?"

He made a grunt. "Here," he said. He motioned with his hand to the turn off onto Prosperity Farms Road. I floated the car into a turn and looked along the side of the road for the place where the oak trees were. I turned right over the small bridge which led over the canal and into the parking lot. This handsome business court was one of the first on Prosperity Farms Road and I'd always remembered it fondly because of the intertwining boughs of the oak trees and their welcoming shade. The clouds were still full but it hadn't yet rained. We closed up the car and went up the concrete stairs to the Healthplex and into the large reception area.

A lithe, middle-aged receptionist was standing behind the desk and asked us to sign in.

"Do they have the two massage tables?" I asked.

"Two tables?"

"Yes, it's for both of us at the same time. In the same room."

"Let me check."

She walked around the front of the desk and down the long carpeted hall which had treatment rooms and offices on either side. Alice Quaid, a craniosacral therapist who had worked on Dad the year before, entered from down the hall to drop off some papers. We both liked her. She had freckles and short, dark rich hair and spoke in the lilting accent of her native New Orleans. Originally a physical therapist, she worked mostly on infants and toddlers at the Healthplex Clinic. She recognized Dad and asked about his hat.

"Were you on that submarine?"

"Yes," he said. "You just had to watch it when you submerged."

Alice smiled. "Did the dishes go flying?"

"Not in the mess hall. They were tied down. But some of the chairs did."

She told us she'd heard in the back about what we were planning on doing and said she wished she were the one working on us, gave us both a hug, and went off to her next appointment.

The Healthplex Clinic at the Upledger Institute is considered by locals as a mecca for something called, "Craniosacral Therapy." As hard as it may be to pronounce, this hands-on healing art works with gently loosening the soft tissue structures around the brain, spinal cord, and central nervous system. It does this by using a very light touch, which can be very pleasant in itself. This is neither brain surgery, nor bone crunching, nor high velocity neck and back adjustments, it's simple, hands-on, nonintrusive, and high intentioned touch. That's about it. It works not just with one isolated part of the body, not just with the whole, but with both, the part and the whole.

This light touch can gently unlock the fluid channels around the head, or cranium, and around the tailbone, or sacrum. We all know what a cranium is, if just from the board game, Cranium™ that's been featured at every Starbucks on the planet by now, and the sacrum is the flat triangular bone at the base of the spine. If you place the flat of your hand at the base of your spine, you can feel the sacrum, it's the foundation bone of the spine, or as it was once called long ago, the "sacred bone." So however difficult the pronunciation, it makes sense, "cranium" and "sacrum," cranio and sacral. And all together it makes up what's called the craniosacral system. In my modest practice, based more in Los Angeles now, but that could always change, I tell people to picture a delicate flower inside the cranium with a very long stem that goes all the way down to the earth, or sacrum, where it plants. The flower has fluid in it too, which nourishes it. Besides feeling like heaven on earth, craniosacral therapy unlocks, opens, and releases the fluids that surround, cushion, and nourish the delicate tissues of the head and all down the back to get everything flowing, and yes, receiving an hour long session can feel like the whole central nervous system is receiving a warm bath. A craniosacral therapist is trained to work with "no agenda", and as these fluids unlock and open, stubborn emotions that have been long held deep within these structures can begin to gently unlock and safely open also. And in my parlance, the flower wakes up and begins to blossom in the sunlight.

Dad and I were expectant and filled with bright anticipation. Neither of us knew what was going to happen or what we would discover, but what did we have to lose? If nothing else, we each looked forward to a relaxing hour on a massage table. But it was taking them awhile to set the room up for us and I remembered it was a bit of a chore to describe this to them on the phone. We took a seat in the lobby over by the fish tank and looked at the colorful saltwater fish for awhile. Dad said, "It's a money pit here."

"No, no Dad, don't look at it like a money pit." I thought of the cost of courses I'd taken here. It was cheaper than medical school, at least. "Okay, okay, so it may be a money pit and the place a little dysfunctional sometimes, and so what? That's just the Institutional part of the place. That's not the people here. Let's keep an open mind, okay?"

Dad started to nod off. I didn't want his snoring to embarrass me. But old guys do that in the afternoon, they nod off. I looked over at some of the medical books and videos on the small bookshelf next to the fish tank, and thought of Sutherland, Upledger, Barral, and others who had contributed to the field.

I sighed. Who could make sense of all of this? Dad didn't care much about the history or the science, but he still enjoyed receiving the benefits. It seemed to fulcrum, for me in my scant training, mostly around Sutherland and Upledger. But still, there were things that no one would talk about.

Maybe some mysteries are better left alone.

SUTHERLAND AND UPLEDGER

How did this place ever come to be? I wondered for the millionth time.

The way I replayed the story, first came Sutherland, then a bunch of other guys, then Upledger, then a bunch of other guys. And anytime there is a book on the subject, or anywhere near it, Dr. William Garner Sutherland is always mentioned *de rigueur.*

The initial discoveries and secrets of craniosacral were held "behind closed doors" by the English cranial osteopaths in the early part of this century, perhaps because the locals were not ready to receive it. In 1901, the era of Matisse, Kandinsky, Schoenberg, and when Van Gough's paint was wet on the canvas, William Garner Sutherland, DO, while still a student at the first osteopathic college of medicine in the heartland of Missouri, suspected that the bones of the skull could actually move and that this movement, or the lack of it, could possibly affect the rest of the body. He came upon this notion when holding the odd shaped bones of a disarticulated skull in his hands. He had observed some of the sutures to have edges, for example, at the temporoparietal suture, and he hypothesized that the edges of the skull bones themselves could possibly rotate and "unwind" from each other, much like an old fashioned clock band that is wound too tight would unwind.

Dr. Sutherland was part of a great tradition of doctors who would actually experiment on their own bodies first before they would prescribe treatments or medications to others, good

Western doctors such as Samuel Hanheman, Andrew Still, Edmund Bach, Willhelm Reich, and Robert Rhondell Gibson. Story goes, while Dr. Sutherland's wife, Ada, watched and worried, he tested out his hypothesis and would wrap his head very tightly with cloth and vice-like devices of the era such as leather football helmets, to see if the smooth functioning of his body would be affected. It was. His walking was shortly impaired and he developed severe headaches and digestive disorders, to name only a few of his symptoms. Parts of his body had become tight and restricted only because of the pressures he had applied to his head!

You can try this out for yourself, conceivably, although I haven't tried this out for myself and because of this, do not recommend it. I never recommend something I myself have not experienced and include this here merely to illustrate a point: Imagine taking a baseball cap and fitting it very, very tightly around your head for 48 hours. Go about your normal daily activities, including steak dinners, and notice if there is a slight change in the rest of your body. I have tried it for a dinner's worth of time and have felt enough discomfort. Sadly, no one ever tried even this, no one applauded, no one would believe that the bones of the skull could move.

Sutherland was mercilessly criticized by his own contemporaries and his discoveries went underground to be practiced by hush-hush disciples as a closely guarded secret with some exiling themselves to work in England. Others of his disciples stood their ground to work only on infants because no one could possibly disagree that the bones of the infant skull are soft, fontanelles, and have motion.

Social philosopher and historian Arnold Toynbee observed it takes 150 years for a seed idea to come into use by the common populace, and although this observation could possibly be mod-

ified with the introduction of the Internet on a global scale, de-
rivatives of Sutherland's secret school gradually appeared on the
scene: Maura and Franklyn Sills's Karuna Institute — Craniosacral
Biodynamics, Dr. Jim Jealous's school of cranial osteopathy — re-
served exclusively for medical students, and Dr. John Upledger's
school of craniosacral therapy.

Sutherland had been influenced by Dr. Andrew Still, the father of osteopathy and the creator of the first school of osteopathy, *The American School of Osteopathy,* in Kirksville, Missouri. Dr.
Still had asked this question: How could we get sick in one part
of our body without the rest of our body being affected? It just
didn't make sense to him, otherwise. He grew up in farm country and could observe that if one part of a summer crop was
blighted, the whole field might have to be treated, not just the
part. Dr. Still later felt inspired to treat the body as a unified
whole, a unit, and so began the science of osteopathy, "osteo" from
the Greek, meaning "bone." He had also observed, as had other
legendary figures in the medical science of the time, that, as miraculous as it may seem, the body had a marvelous ability to correct itself, and this continues to be referred to as the "self corrective mechanism," or, the "self corrective ability" of the body. Naturally, this is what the body does to maintain its essential balance,
or, *homeostasis,* each moment of every day. Dr. Still determined to
trust in the self corrective ability of the body, and, rather than interfere with it, find ways to support it. The body could find its
way back to health and harmony mostly on its own, if given the
chance. These remain revolutionary ideas in Western Medicine
today, more than a hundred years later!

The way I'd replay the story, in the 1970s, well after the
introduction of relativity theory and quantum mechanics, Andy
Warhol, Rauschenberg, Jonathan Livingston Seagull, and while
the turbulent events of the '60s were still on simmer, John

Upledger DO, OMM, an osteopath himself, happened to observe an odd fluctuation along the spinal cord while assisting in a fairly routine surgery on the spine, but he couldn't identify what this fluctuation was and no one else could either. The fluctuation haunted him, he hadn't been taught about this in medical school, and he eventually sought out the teachings of the guarded, cranial osteopaths, now known as the Cranial Academy. They knew about it, the fluctuations resulted from the inherent motion of fluids within something called the craniosacral system. Upledger studied with them for awhile but felt there was always something lacking in their approach and he soon parted ways.

Upledger was deeply influenced by Dr. Andrew Still, as is common with osteopaths, and by Dr. Sutherland, but Upledger was quickly branded an upstart for his deeper explorations by the more conservative osteopaths, echoing Sutherland's own frustration of long ago. The way I look at this falling out, Upledger showed up on the scene somewhat as an artist would breaking with old forms and tyrannies to express an artistic freedom. His discoveries would occur along with other discoveries in an emerging field called somatics in the seventies and eighties, Jean Paul Barral's Visceral Manipulation™, Ida Rolf's Rolfing™, Moshe Feldenkrais's Feldenkrais®, Ilana Rubenfeld's Synergy Method™, Arnold Mindell's Dreambody and Process Work, Fritz Smith's Zero Balancing, Reiki, Energy Work.

Decades after Sutherland's professional branding, Upledger discovered there was an emotional component within the motion of the skull bones, and in the late 1970s, openly announced to the medical community that the craniosacral system was the physiological system where the body, mind, and spirit integrated and the field burst open like a butterfly. He boldly made his findings public, expanding and developing the field making it available to virtually anyone with good heart and hands, and

despite the harsh and continuing criticism from the entrenched
osteopathic community, he offered solid, well researched courses
orientated toward clinicians and everybody came to find out, including medical doctors, psychiatrists, dentists, registered
nurses, chiropractors, acupuncturists, physical therapists, rolfers,
massage therapists, and even osteopaths. He dubbed his new
synthesis Craniosacral Therapy to distinguish it from psychoso-
matic allopathic approaches of the time — say those multi-syllabic
jewels three times very fast without smiling, and although still under fire, he is credited by less conservative osteopaths for
having taken the field out of the closet and for breathing new life
in it.

"So is it osteopathy?" I'd often been asked.

Very different.

Although some of the lines of demarcation are starting to
blur with the introduction of craniosacral therapy, and although
both approaches aim to work with the part and with the whole
rather than with isolated systems in the body, this first differs
from cranial osteopathy in that it openly acknowledges there is
an inner emotional world to each person and that it's all right
to have one. Secondly, Craniosacral Therapy acknowledges the
appropriate release of emotion during sessions where Cranial
Osteopathy does not permit this. Cranial Osteopathy cautions
patients to allow any emotional releases that may arise during
sessions only until later on, preferably in the presence of a psychiatrist or counselor. Third, another difference is that unlike
the cranial osteopath, the focus is not on the direct, outer
manipulation of the cranial bones, or for example, the taking of
physical measurements of the alignment of the spine or posture,
rather, it works from the inside out and allows the delicate connective tissue membranes, called meningial membranes, from
within the spine to move just how they want and need to move

and when. Upledger has said he cannot presume to know the way a bone in the skull "should" move. Very different in orientation. The craniosacral therapist works with the outer landmarks of the skull as bony handles only to attune with the deeper connective tissue structures of the craniosacral system within, our living flower.

I haven't yet read Dr. William Garner Sutherland's work in depth, but for an account of his initial discoveries, the reader would do well to look for a charming book written in true Victorian style by his wife, Ada Sutherland (also his first student), *With Thinking Fingers,* and for a compilation of his final lectures, *Teachings in the Science of Osteopathy.* And an interested reader could do no better than go to Dr. Upledger's own accounts of his discoveries and development of Upledger Craniosacral Therapy in his books, *Craniosacral Therapy: Touchstone for Natural Healing,* also, *Cell Talk,* which uncovers new research with the Immune System and with the Brain and reveals a deeper approach to the interior world and its mysteries. There are of course several other wonderful and fascinating schools of craniosacral including Franklyn Sill's Craniosacral Biodynamics, Hugh Milne's Visionary Craniosacral, and the Osho school of Craniosacral, but to describe them here and their differences, as tempting as this may be, would take us far from the aim of this book.

Again, it really didn't matter to Dad who came up with it, all that really mattered was that it worked and we were here together.

"YE ARE GODS"

The receptionist returned and smiled, "We're ready for you now."

I warmly thanked her and we followed her back. Dad and I walked side by side and looked into the rooms that were open with nobody inside. I hoped he wouldn't mind the expense. He'd always complained that this place was too expensive and I'd have to say that it was much less than he'd ever paid to his doctors or lawyers. "And how much better do you feel after your lawyers get done with you?" My hand reached up and touched the back of his wrist. There was a massage therapist down the hall with long blonde hair and blue eyes that I'd wanted him to meet for visits to the house when I was out of town. "That's that massage therapist," I whispered. "Has the same name as my ex-girlfriend, Susan."

"Susan?" he asked, too loud.

But she was occupied in conversation and didn't turn around. Moments later, we saw the first of what was to be our two therapists walking out the doors at the farther end of the hall. She moved with grace and confidence and although new to the Healthplex Clinic, I felt glad that she was available that day. Her name was Sheryl.

Dad motioned to Sheryl, "She's more important."

"She is," to avoid argument.

Sheryl was an occupational therapist with well kempt brown hair and inquiring eyes and like all of the women here wore slacks and hospital shoes. I'd had the privilege of working alongside of her when assisting here for my schooling and trusted her.

"Hi, so is it the two of you?" she asked.

We smiled to each other sheepishly and the receptionist departed. We went into our treatment room. I was glad to see they'd followed my instructions and placed the two massage tables side by side. Sheryl checked her notes, then stepped out as Dad pulled off his clothes, stripping down to his boxers and T-shirt. Chas Perry, our other therapist, looked in briefly and stepped back out to the hall. He has a warm and smiling face with a ruddy complexion and long shocks of white hair and crystal clear eyes. I took my shoes and my belt off and Dad was already on his table. It looked like he was into his nap and would start to snore. I wasn't sure if to get on the other table. I wanted to ask Dad if he was ready for this, but here we were.

"Wherever you are, Dad…"

"There you are!"

He was awake.

It was a phrase that both of us picked up from when I talked him into going with me to see the cremation of that Tibetan lama in Vermont, Chogyam Trungpa Rinpoche.

Dad and I kept getting lost in the hills in our rental car and missed some of the ceremonies and couldn't find where the Buddhas were and all we could figure after awhile was, wherever you are, there you are. It was originally from poet Bodhisattvas and tossed around by Trungpa's more literary devotees. The trick was always to place the line emphasis on the second YOU. We'd say that second YOU to each other's faces in the chilly car and laugh!

Chas and Sheryl came back and introduced themselves. I guessed Chas would be the lead therapist and Sheryl would assist. I'd known "Chas" Perry as an instructor in most my craniosacral therapy courses. He'd had a Ph.D. in Philosophy—or in Somatics, depending on who you spoke to—and he'd said he saw the practice of this hands-on healing art as an evolution of his studies. I breathed a sigh of relief. The session had started.

"So you're doing this together," said Chas with a smile.

"It's sort of a father and son thing," I answered. "Father and son, pals forever."

Chas gave a warm laugh and looked at Dad, who was face up on the lambskin massage table in his boxers. "Father and son?"

"Father and son," said Dad.

"Okay, it's a father and son session!" said Chas.

We all laughed. The tables had been set side by side and the mood was warm. Sheryl sat demurely in one of the dark, comfortable chairs. I got up on the table next to Dad and tried to focus on the ceiling. Sheryl placed her hands gently under the back of Dad's neck and head, and Chas held the sides of Dad's feet. Then Chas visited with me, placing hands at my ankles. The feeling in my body was suddenly warm with a certain light heartedness. It's always this way when another touches us with a loving intention and without expectation of personal gain, a space opens to the simple feeling of being. Then Sheryl visited with me and Chas went back to Dad. They were to change positions every now and then but it ended up that Chas was mostly with Dad and Sheryl with me, and what did it matter? For us, it was all about the living space that held us both, that's what was to guide the session to follow, our relationship.

"It's not to make a big agenda or anything, it's just to work with the space that surrounds us," I offered.

"I want him to stop smoking," said Dad abruptly.

"I've actually cut down."

Chas and Sheryl looked over the tables at each other and smiled.

Chas addressed me. "Has he ever had this kind of work before?"

"Yes, but it's family."

Dad was about the only family member I could work on, it was a lot harder to work on my sisters. Even spiritual healers avoid work on family members. And most surgeons won't operate on their children. Too much stuff gets in the way.

Chas and Sheryl were concentrated and soon time itself seemed to stretch and slow down. My body felt deeply relaxed yet light on the massage table. We were moving and merging into a quiet blend of hearts and minds.

This is also the way things are, all of the time, if we would only give ourselves a chance to slow down long enough to find out. I could hardly believe I was relaxing into this feeling of *blending* in a session with Dad! I could almost let myself go inside the very light touch. What would happen next? It's the feeling of taking a nap on a weekend afternoon next to a trusted family member or a good friend or pet. It's the feeling of quietly sitting at table with others, or watching the Superbowl on TV, or an inspiring sermon, or a great poet, or the Academy Awards, knowing there are thousands of others watching along with you. And there is a very large array of experiences, frequencies, energies, vibes, available to each of one us when we are in touch with our more subtle feelings. Just slow down long enough to be where you are. Take the time to notice there are others around you. Blending or *melding* was thankfully developed as a specific technique by Dr. Upledger for his craniosacral therapists. It's not like thinking. There's no effort. It's not a trance-state, one is very aware, and it's not a raw emotional-state. It's based on the language of feeling, and for me, almost a *feeling-into* frequency. Blending is always available, always mutual, and based on a quiet cooperation and a meeting of hearts and minds.

At these times, it's a useful reminder that there is no interaction in the visible world that is not also based on a corresponding and mutual interaction in the invisible.

Most of us may not think we have the personal bandwidth to attune to blending, but it's not so hard to conceive. If a television set were placed in this same clinic room, there would be a number of frequencies available to us to tune into to watch the different TV shows, or if a radio receiver, hundreds of stations to play. All we'd have to do is push the button on the remote. A vast number of frequencies are zipping through the space around us and available to us all of the time. Why not the blending frequency? I smiled. I could feel my body relax into a deeper sigh.

Chas said, "Was there anything you two wanted to go over with each other?"

Silence. Then. Dad said, "Well, I spanked him when he was a kid."

I said, slowly, "Yeah, we didn't used to get along so well. But we do now."

Chas said, "Anything about that?"

Dad didn't answer.

I said, "Well..."

Chas said, a smile in his voice, "It seems he's fine with it. Are you still carrying a piece of that?"

I smiled to myself. It seemed the Father was fine with it and the Son was still carrying a bit of it. I couldn't remember him spanking me hardly. I remembered Mom chasing me up the stairs with a skimpy wire coat hanger. Then Dad started to talk about Mom and the therapists receded to the background, to become almost invisible.

Held in a space of such attention, Dad let out some pain, some quiet sorrow. "She was the best. Because of her, I was a success in the law and then in the property. She raised seven children. The best."

Minutes passed in this expanded space.

"I'm grateful to be with you, Dad. Grateful you're here. We've grown."

"Yeah, our relationship changed after we saw the Buddhas."

"The Buddhas."

"You wouldn't let me videotape you in that hall."

"You were supposed to bow down, like everybody else...I guess."

"We took it from the pedestal and put it on the floor."

"I didn't quite get that," said Chas. "You took what...?"

"He means, about the Buddhas, the Lamas, all that. They were all higher up than everybody else. They were sitting on big chairs. They liked him."

Chas looked to Sheryl, who shrugged her shoulders.

I could feel my whole body smile.

He said, "I tell it like it is."

Then a thought occurred to me. It was as if Dad was still on that pedestal. Or maybe I'd put him up there. But he'd never come down from it. Ever since I was a kid, he was so much taller than me. So far away. It confused me. "You made yourself out to be God."

"*He's* far away from me. I'm just here."

My thought about Dad on a pedestal continued. I slowly spoke it out loud, a tape inside my head. "And I made these other Gods. I made John Upledger into a God when I was here, and Burt Reynolds into a God when I was an apprentice at his theater over there. Then later, Burt was part of my one man show, at the very end when I was in despair and tried to pray to God, the God, but got all these other names mixed in with...idols and others...." The thought had exhausted its content. My neck relaxed and my head turned to one side, imperceptibly, as if by itself, in the silence.

"You don't finish things."

"I didn't finish my acting career."

A deeper silence. All along our legs were touching and we were hand in hand.

Another thought occurred. "All the girls between us. They always said what you wanted back to me. And what they said wasn't always true. I've been living by myself for so many years. Mom said, 'Why does our son have to be so alone!' I've never even proposed to a woman."

"Why not?" asked Dad.

"The girls. They always ended up being my sisters." I could feel the Therapists smile to each other. I didn't mind it. It just didn't seem I was communicating very well. "I just wanted to be with you, even to be you. You were so far away."

"You go with the girls. They really like you. Those blue eyes."

I tried not to think of my looks. I was overweight as a kid with big ears and the image sort of stuck, even when my hair turned blonde from surfing. I wasn't used to being considered handsome and it took me years to figure out I might be. "The sisters. I let the sisters beat up on me, they were between us."

Dad laughed. "If you don't have the girls to beat up on you, you go with the girl to beat you up."

"Whaat?"

The therapists laughed and Dad laughed. I couldn't conceal a smile.

Susan would yell at me. The movie inside my head played on, and every now and then I'd look at a scene from it as it rolled by on the screen. After we broke up in L.A., a craniosacral therapist gently gathered the noise of Susan's yelling from out my temporal bones, around my ears, and sent it harmlessly away from my body. There's an old Italian saying that the devil is in the noise. The noise of Susan's yelling had lodged in my ears almost as a cyst of energy. The therapist was Sheru Hurlong, DO, then in her fourth year of medical school as an osteopath, and I remain grateful to her for removing the "cyst." But Susan? Not my type. Not now. Dad had met Susan.

"You were always so far away."

And Dad said, "I've always wanted the best for you. And what you wanted to do."

And I said, "You mean, you're on my side?"

"I've always been on your side. I've always believed in you."

Chas suggested, "You feel that he's already a success? Just by who he is?"

"Yeah. And he has potential. I want him to express that."

"I have been expressing it."

And Chas and Sheryl quietly shared another warm laugh.

After awhile, Chas said, "Any piece you want to say? It seems he's fine with your relationship."

Tears formed along the edges of my eyes. "He's my best friend."

Chas said, "Do you hear that? He says you're his best friend."

Dad said, "We're friends."

Chas said, "Friends other than father and son?"

And Dad said, "Yes."

Some minutes passed in the deeper silences that followed. At the beginning of his life, Dad worked as a carpenter. I could feel the warmth of his wide palm and thick fingers intertwined with mine. I couldn't move my hand from his or wouldn't. My hand felt small. Then another thought surfaced and I rambled about how I was tired of California and didn't make it as an actor or get married out there and thought from talking with Dad that I had to be a big success like him before I could ever get married and maybe I was a little afraid of it and the whole room listened.

Dad said, "I'm a success."

"You are," Sheryl said.

"Everything I touch prospers. The law practice and the prop-erties. It doesn't stop at the properties, it goes on. I started the

Heart Association, the Cancer Society, the Opera. I was Chairman of the Salvation Army Ball, but that was with Momma."

He quieted, the pain again.

My eyes were closed. My shoulders and head rolled toward him, as if of their own volition. And I felt my leg move up and over to rest comfortably on his leg, our ankles intertwined. Bodies do this in this deeper warmth if we let them.

"We're always growing and evolving," I heard myself say.

What Dad said next came out of nowhere.

"You are God. And I am God. ...What does it say in the Bible about that?"

I'd never heard him say that. Never in my entire life. Then I felt a flush of warmth course through my whole chest. Where did it say that in the Bible? "'Ye are Gods,' it says."

"Says that?"

"Yeah. New Testament. You are God. And I am God. We are Gods."

A silence filled the room.

He said, "Okay, I've exposed myself. Are we about done?"

Chas answered, "You exposed yourself."

Dad said, "Yes."

And we all laughed now. The session was over.

TRULY HAPPY

Or was the session just beginning? Not on a relaxing treatment table with two thoughtful therapists, but in real life? Certain sessions can be like the fabled pebble that drops in a pond, and the ripples can be felt for days, weeks, months, and even beyond.

Driving to Ballen Isles for an early supper, Dad said, "I feel great."

"Me too." The heavy clouds had unloaded their fill and the sky was fresh with new possibility.

"I don't feel that I have to tighten up when I talk with you, or be concerned about saying the wrong thing."

I was sorry he'd felt that way before. "I'm grateful to hear that, Dad."

"We should have done this years ago."

"We weren't just reacting. Were we?"

"No, we weren't."

There was a silence. "I just found out you could do it recently. I did it in a class with Chas. We did it as an experiment with this young married couple. We did it with them on two massage tables. It was up at the Esalen Institute in Big Sur."

"Oh, the Big Sur."

Dad and Mom and I had taken a trip there from L.A. one Christmas, just the three of us, and they loved it. The streets of San Luis Obisbo, Big Sur, and Carmel were deserted that time of year and we had the coast road all to ourselves. Then I got it into my head to get them both up to Gilroy at the same time, the garlic capital of the world, to visit with an old man, a retired chiropractor, I knew. Mom had heard this man speak on an audiotape and sort of got what his information meant to me but I thought Dad would not go for it one bit. Just outside of Gilroy, I was driving the rental car so fast I got pulled over for a speeding ticket. We spent a miserable night in the fog lost outside Stockton, miles from Gilroy.

The well dressed valet took the car at Ballen Isles. Dad held my arm for support as we went up the small flight of steps, down the hall with its tinted Masters photographs of Arnold Palmer, Jack Nicholas, Bob Hope, and into the sumptuous dining room. We sat but then decided on the buffet.

Dad sipped iced tea. "When my rehab starts, I might try hitting a few golf balls."

"That would be great," I said. "Maybe I'll join you, if you like."

He didn't say no but looked out at the wide grass lawns.

I felt truly happy.

That night we were both on Dad's bed in his bedroom and watching a show on Alfred Hitchcock's life. Dad was under the covers with his head propped up on a pillow, half asleep. I was over on Mom's side of the bed and my shoes were still on. The television was too loud but Dad likes it that way. The air conditioner and fan were on full blast. Dad pulled the covers aside and slung his feet over to sit on the edge of the bed. His shoulders were slumped and he almost looked frail.

"I'm more tired than I thought," he said.

"Yeah?"

He put a hand through his thinning hair and said, "What about medical school?"

"I've thought about it."

"You could do osteopathy, if there's a two or three year program here or in Europe."

"Yeah, maybe."

"That's what this work is based on," he said.

"True...I never would have heard of osteopathy if it weren't for this." Then I cringed. I'd flashed on an image of an osteopath with gray hair and ashen face sitting alone in a cluttered office on Dixie Highway that I once went to visit with Dad. The fellow seemed kind enough. Dad went in for his treatment and came back out a few minutes later and headed for the door. I was surprised how short the treatment was but was glad to get out of there. "If I went to osteopathy school, it would be more education. More years."

"In high school, son, the administration took my class on a field trip to see a Shakespeare play. And on the outside of the theater before we went in was inscribed these few words, in stone, 'Ye yourself must set fire to the faggots which ye have brought."

"I know," I said. I'd heard it before.

"Set yourself on fire! I never forgot this, 'Ye yourself.'"

"Maybe I could do it. I don't know if I have the math for it."

"You took those nurses courses. Premed, that counts. And they gave you honors, how about that?"

"But that was just science. It wasn't math."

"Do something!"

"I'm writing my plays, Dad."

He wasn't impressed.

MY LIFE GOES OFF TRACK

Do something.

He went to the bathroom and I got up to go to bed. Alfred Hitchcock was being interviewed and there was a close up of him pointing to his round forehead. I felt the heat of the house as soon as I went up the stairs to my room. I heard the sound of the television through the floorboards. There was a breeze from the ocean and I opened both my windows all the way to let it in. It was at least a mild summer, not as hot as those I'd grown up with at the house, and we'd only installed a few air conditioners in the last ten years or so. I liked the heat in my room. I took a pen and sat on the edge of my bed. I picked up my journal and started to write down the events of the day. I find it's always a good idea after sessions anyway. I simply write down the events without writing down my opinions of the events or what I might feel ought to have happened. This way, when I return to my journal entry months or years later, I can reread it from where I am now rather than from where I was then, and still take something from it, some lesson. As I dotted the last i and crossed the last T, I tried to remember what had happened to me and I thought of the color blue.

It wasn't anything I could tell Dad about, and I wasn't sure I understood it myself. Were those who had this light shade of ice blue, or color of deep, indigo in their core, special? Mom knew. I turned in my journal to a passage I'd scribbled by my favorite poet of the time, Rumi.

This piece of food cannot be eaten,
nor this bit of wisdom found by looking.
There is a secret core in everyone not
even Gabriel can know by trying to know.

Was it appropriate to tell anyone about this? It couldn't be patented or traded or codified. Not everyone had it. It was simply absent from them, as if it had never had a chance to grow inside their core. I'd always seen it just from the corner of my eye and always during sessions, blue. Blue like the ocean but within a living human being. Animals had it too, dogs, cats, horses, and I could see it, if I tuned into them with a kind of second attention.

I looked around my room for other journal notes, notes from when I first went out to California in search of God and an acting career, so long ago. I walked quietly from shelf to drawer so I wouldn't wake Dad. But what I found were plays and ideas for plays I hadn't finished or produced, a torment of plays and poems everywhere. What had happened to me? How did I end up touching people with my hands? I looked out at the dark ocean and touched my journal. I looked back at my bookshelf. There were the plays I had read, studied, acted in, Shakespeare, Beckett, Miller, so many.

I just didn't know.

Before my life went off track, I'd supported my interest in theater as a floor clerk working at a bookstore in Los Angeles called the Bodhi Tree. It was my day job for almost eight years. The Bodhi Tree was very 1970s. The great movements of the 1960s and 1970s had died out, Civil Rights, Vietnam war, Sexual Revolution, and Feminism, but I liked the Bodhi Tree because it was a small refuge for one movement that had not died out, the Aquarian or, as it was known in the 1980s, the "New Age" movement. I would come home at night to my lonely apartment and see my computer facing me and there was nothing I could do but write. I had no wife, no children, no social life to speak of and this was something I could do for the moment. The bookstore was a mecca for those interested in things spiritual and filled with thousands of eclectic books with every subject from Astrology to Zen. It was the same bookstore that Shirley MacLaine wandered into when she began her spiritual quest and later wrote about in her best selling book, *Out on a Limb*.

One day, a massage therapist wandered into the bookstore. He had long hair and bohemian style clothes and smelled like patchouli oil. He said he was a master massage therapist. I came out from behind the cash register and helped him to find some aromatherapy oils and he handed me his card. Sure enough, it said, "Master Massage Therapist." This guy intrigued me and I asked him how much he made. He said he made more than five hundred a week. "Five hundred dollars?" I said. That sounded like a lot more than I was making. Later, my back went out during rehearsals for a production on a one man show I'd written entitled, *Sometimes I Can't Tell the Difference Between L.A. and My Mind!*, and a friend suggested I get in touch with this old man in Northern California. He'd fix it.

I called him on the phone, and there was a feeling about this man and a presence I could feel from the distance of L.A. I hoped he wouldn't become another one of those names I would pray to when I was confused by despair, like at the end of the one man show. I was scared about meeting him but in too much pain to say no.

II

Presence

THE OLD MAN
IN NORTHERN CALIFORNIA

We were in a cafe in Gilroy, California. Gilroy is the garlic capital of the world. Some people find it amusing when I tell them that Gilroy is where the old man lived. I guess because garlic is supposed to keep away vampires. He was sitting across the booth from me and smoking a Tareyton cigarette. We'd ordered coffee. The waitress had a pencil stuck behind her bun and wore a pink skirt with an apron. The old man wasn't so impressive to look at himself. Then again, much later I would see him point out to others like myself, on another occasion, that it's the contents that matter, not the container. He had a cream colored sport coat on, but I noticed one of the buttons from his white shirt was missing. He had deep blue eyes that seemed to see right through me to my toes. His facial skin was ruddy and pock marked and his left eye seemed to wander. He reminded me of Anthony Quinn in Zorba, the Greek but with white fluffy hair. I felt a little awkward.

"How ya doin'?" said the waitress.

He said, "Couldn't be better."

The waitress seemed to like that.

I smiled politely.

He said, "Well, I couldn't be better than I am right now. Could you?"

"I could always be better," I said.

"How 'bout at this moment?"

I didn't know what to say. Words somehow eluded me. "I

guess not."

He smiled and took a drag on his cigarette.

Secretly, I wanted one too. But I'd been around famous spiritual teachers and studies in consciousness for quite a while and, as jaded as I was, Tareyton cigarettes didn't seem all that spiritual. These were the days when you could still smoke in restaurants in California. I felt deeply challenged.

I'd originally heard about this man from a writer friend of mine who now lives in Ojai, California, a small town just outside of L.A. She'd been a psych major at Stanford and I admired her for that, but more for having been published in impressive sounding national literary quarterlies. She had a quick intelligence and I trusted her. She told me she'd been visiting her brother in San Francisco and they were driving in his car. He'd been in Narcotics Anonymous (NA), and she noticed he had some loose leaf notes on the floor under his passenger seat. She got curious. She reached down and sneaked a peek to see what he was into and then she started to get interested. She flipped through the notes and said, "This is just like Krishnamurti! Where did you get this stuff?"

"Oh, this old guy," he said.

She'd been a huge J. Krishnamurti fan for years. Her brother didn't seem to know who J. Krishnamurti was. J. Krishnamurti was considered by many to be a spiritual teacher of the highest order and a guide of the age. He refused to be seen by thousands of would be followers as an authority and he refused disciples. He passed away in 1986, but Ojai was his home base and primary place of residence.

There had been a question and I remembered it now. I hoped it would make sense. It was almost as if I couldn't locate the words.

"How do you know what you want to do? Like, your direction in life? Just what you want to do?"

"You know by what you're doin'," he said.

I had no idea what he meant.

He smiled and looked out the window at the cars.

"Thank you," I said.

I took a sip of the coffee. I was feeling warm and pleasant. Thank you. I was a blank. Discursive thoughts couldn't connect to my mouth around him. Thank you, was all I could hear. For some reason I remembered a gruesome photo on the front page of the *Los Angeles Times* I'd seen on the drive up.

I said, "Did you see that photo in the paper?"

"What's that?"

"You read the paper?"

"Classifieds is the only news. Shows you what everybody is doing around town," he said.

"Yeah, but this photo, it was awful. Front page."

For a moment, I couldn't remember what the photo was. I made an effort to remember. It was of a truck that had crashed through the glass window of a store. The article was about a man who had killed his wife and two children and then shot himself. He shot himself while he was driving in his truck. I described it as best I could. He didn't seem alarmed.

"Yep. That's what they do," he said.

I wondered if I'd said anything wrong, but it made so much sense. Stories like these were everywhere in the news, of people killing others and then killing themselves. Terrible, violent deaths in a civilization which tries to pass itself off as a culture. That's what they do, I very slowly heard in my mind. That's what they do.

The man's presence was radiating everywhere. I mean, when we first walked into this roadside restaurant cafe there were two or three people in there and everyone looked sour in the mouth. It was around eight o'clock in the evening.

I'd made the trip up from L.A. that day. I could hardly walk. My lower back had been twisted out like a pretzel. I couldn't find a decent chiropractor to take care of it without it hurting more and I was spending more money than I wanted to. Someone told me this man had once been a chiropractor. He said he'd fix it, but I'd have to make the trip up there. I drove up to Gilroy in tremendous pain. He was outside on the carport when I drove up the drive.

"What took you so long?" he asked.

"Pain," I said.

He invited me inside and asked me to sit down. He stepped behind me and he fixed it in a moment. Hardly without touching me. Just a simple adjust and then I felt whomped with wave after wave of nourishing and nurturing energies. It was almost as if I could see waves of color in the room, of violet, pink, and dark green. And I never saw any colors, I wasn't the type to see colors. There was a sharp twinge but I could get up and walk and was soon without discomfort.

"How much?" I asked him.

"Ten dollars is fine."

Afterwards we went out to eat and he asked what I was in the mood for. I said something like, wherever the food is good.

He said, "There's no good restaurants in Gilroy."

We hadn't been in the empty restaurant for twenty minutes before it filled to the max and everyone was chatting up a storm. I couldn't believe how loud and crowded the place had gotten and that so many people were all in such a pleasant and delightful mood all at once. It was like a party and everyone was invited.

"Look at all these people," I said. "What are they doing here?"

"Birds of a feather."

I wanted to say something, but it was too difficult to finish full sentences around him. "Bird," I said.

"Happens every time I go into a restaurant. It fills up."

"Birds," I said again. "Flock together."

He took the check and paid for the food.

Not too many years later, I asked him a question. "People have asked about you, like my family. If anyone ever asks me to describe you, what would I say?"

He cleared his throat. "Just an old man up in Northern California doin' his own thing."

Otherwise, it was to consider him as a friend.

I told him about my interest in massage therapy and asked, "What about getting a license?" I asked.

He said "Leave it alone, for now."

He set the tone for my adventure to come.

WORKING WITH PEOPLE

Two weeks later, I grabbed a friend of a friend who was visiting from Taos, New Mexico, and I asked her to teach me some of what she did. I'd heard she'd been practicing Shiatsu for years and she was kind enough to give me some essential pointers on her art.

It took me awhile to find her friend's place where she was visiting, and it wasn't in an area of Hollywood I really approved of. It was around Vine and Lexington, not in Beverly Hills, and most of the houses were rundown looking. I parked my car and locked it up and when I rang on the doorbell there was no answer. I turned to leave and get out of there but then I heard a warm and friendly voice inviting me in. Glenda was at the door. She was a commanding presence and a strong woman and led me through the afternoon shadows into a cluttered but comfortable living room. She invited me to sit on a red pillow on the floor.

As she showed me the pressure points, she said she was amazed at how quickly I sensed them. This surprised me. It seemed so easy. I had no idea I might have any talent at this, but she said my fingers went exactly to the points and stayed on them just as long as they needed to. After awhile, I would work on her with one hand, and try to take notes and draw pictures of the body with the Shiatsu points on sheets of paper spread on the floor. I thought of the theater and wondered if I was somehow about to betray it?

What had always interested me about theater was not the

bright lights or the words of the plays so much as the almost intuitive quality of the space of the theater itself. To make a theater, all anyone needs is an empty space and at least one actor or
actress to act on it. Was it the being in front of the audience with
the bright lights that got me going or was it the silences and intervals of silence in the classes, offstage? Could it be that acting
was a healing journey in itself? Or a preparation for this line of
work? What other actors and actresses had made the discovery
of their power to heal? I didn't share any of this with her aloud.
It seemed I was getting it, or that my hands were getting it, and
I was beginning to feel a little nervous. I confessed to her that I
was worried about not knowing anatomy. She said I would learn
the anatomy through my hands and through my work and not to
worry about it. She said she learned her anatomy by working as
a butcher.

"The anatomy isn't all that different."

"Really?" I said. "No shit."

I told her I was worried about getting a license to practice
massage as I'd never had any formal training. She said that she'd
never had a license in all her years of practice and had been able
to maintain a ranch in Taos. She even worked on movie stars. I
was very impressed. But I still wasn't sure. She put her hands on
my shoulders and looked straight into my eyes. She was an older woman with silver hair and looked and smelled like an earth
mother.

"Tell me, are you working with the government or are you
working with people?"

"People," I answered.

From then on, whenever anybody came into the bookstore
who was in the midst of a personal or spiritual crisis, I would
hand them a massage card and say, "How about a nurturing massage?" It was bit spartan, I admit, but it worked! I'd go to their

homes, set up a blanket or two on the floor, kneel down, and do my Shiatsu moves. Soon I'd combine it with massage. I'd rent the videos at the bookstore on massage and study the massage moves in the books we had on the shelves. I'd even call up the authors of the books and ask them questions. And all of them agreed that the main thing was to work on people. So I did.

CHIROPRACTOR ON MELROSE

My one Shiatsu lesson with the butcher from Taos gave me confidence, and the work I was doing began to quickly evolve from the ground up. It wasn't long before my own personal chiropractor took an interest in the work I was doing. His office was located directly across the street from the Bodhi Tree and his name was Dr. Robert Galas. He had light shoulder length hair, a gentle and soft spoken way about him, thumbs of iron, and the one chiropractor that the staff of the Bodhi Tree would return to again and again over the years. Before I started doing bodywork and massage, I wouldn't go in that much, maybe once or twice a year, because I'd always been leery of chiropractors. And I didn't go to his office after my back went out for my one man show because I just didn't think to go there. Whenever I went to a chiropractor it felt like I was doing something horribly wrong, something that was disapproved of by society. But my back would hurt so much that after awhile, there was nowhere else I could go if I wanted to avoid surgery, and I'd actually feel better.

Now, from my long hours standing at the bookstore and from bending over and doing work on people's floors, my back began to hurt and I'd sneak across the street to his office a little more than before. The office lobby wasn't much to look at. There weren't any plants or handsome lights on the walls like there are now. There were framed pictures, but they were mostly stacked up in the hallways. Dr. Galas had inherited this office from an older chiropractor, his senior, and it was once a sought after location where fashion models, television and movie stars regularly attended, but since Dr. Galas's mentor passed on, it was in shadow. Dr. Galas managed to light up the place with his pleasant manner, but I still couldn't get past the taboo of going to a chiropractor and mostly stayed away.

Around this time, I attended a public talk that the old man from Northern California was giving at a small trailer park resort in Laguna Beach. About fifty people were there and at the end of the afternoon talk a few participants lined up for him to give them a special neck adjustment. It was a favor that he did only for those who asked. I watched what he did and it was then I learned about the two cervical vertebrae at the top of the neck called the atlas and the axis. These two small bones work together in concert, like a fifth wheel which holds a cabin and long haul truck together, and are a key area of the body. The old man told me the atlas and the axis adjustment was the only adjustment the old time chiropractors ever did. Once these two bones were adjusted, the rest of the vertebrae would follow suit like dominoes in a row and this fascinated me.

Seeing this old man whom I respected so much gentled me, and now when I would go down the odd angled hall and slip into Dr. Galas's office and get onto his chiropractic table, the first thing I'd say was just exactly how I wanted the adjustment to be done because of things I'd learned from the old man. I wasn't sure if it would be all right to say anything out loud but its a little known fact that this is the patient's privilege. Dr. Galas wasn't used to doing adjustments like this, the old fashioned way, and between my visits he would go back and consult his more outdated chiropractic books and would be surprised to find that what I was saying was accurate. We'd call my treatments, the old western cowboy treatments, and each time he would considerately stand aside and ask if I wanted the same? I so appreciated this courtesy. It reminded me of my first pediatrician when I was a kid in West Palm Beach, Dr. Eddie Stephens, who was also duck hunting partners with my Dad. "Dr. Eddie" had a soft and gentle manner under his wire rimmed glasses and a wonderful sense of humor that would always make me laugh. Before he'd examine me, he'd always look at me in the eyes for a split second as if to ask my permission. It wasn't anything he'd say out loud. But that meant something to me because I was already put off from smells of the Doctor's office and the cold metal examination table. I didn't know then that I was beginning to learn the value of simple courtesy and good bedside manners. Much later, I'd tell Dad, if Dr. Eddie ever passes on from this world I hope he lets me inherit his bedside manners!

After a year or so of my sneak visits across the street, I was getting more comfortable with chiropractic and one day, Dr. Galas said he needed a staff massage therapist to loosen up people's tight shoulders and necks to prepare them for adjustments.

"Would you be open to that?"

"Sure, I guess," I said, concealing a bewildering excitement.

"Okay. We'll see what happens."

A couple of weeks later he had me in and "auditioned" me for the position of massage therapist by having me go right to work on his clients, and they loved it!

My life was about to never be the same again.

I had happened into a virtual laboratory where I could apply what I was learning from the books, videos, body workers, and massage therapists who happened into the store and, like it or not, I was on my way.

THE BACK ROOM

My laboratory wasn't much to look at. I would lead patients through the oddly angled hallways past the smelly X-Ray room and into a back room. The table I used for my notes was a breakfast table and too large for the room, the bracketed shelves above it were bent from the weight of heavy textbooks, worn chiropractic devices, and odd ceramic objects which, like the breakfast table, were left there from yard sales in the neighborhood. When most patients first came in they stopped, looked at the pink, paint-chipped walls and for a place to sit, but there was no chair. I was just the massage therapist and soon discovered that I was very low on the pecking order. And I did not know then how poorly treated body workers and massage therapists were in spas, I hadn't ever been to a spa in my life. But this looked more like a store room than a treatment room in an acute care clinic. The back room could barely fit the blue lambskin massage table. But I worked at keeping my mood up and tone high, on and off hours, to fill the room with favorable and pleasant energy, just like the old man at the restaurant. I went out and got a deep fleece to wrap around the table and over this, a fresh white sheet was always laid so it was warm and comfortable.

I did three years of intuitive bodywork and massage therapy at the chiropractic clinic before ever taking a formal course. I figured why spend thousands of dollars on massage school first? That would be for later and I'd go to the best school I could. I'd heard stories of massage therapists, even chiropractors, who after years of schooling never set up shop and this was tragic to me. This was my lemonade stand and I was selling the most wonderful massage strokes I could possibly integrate. I'd go to the massage schools and pretend to apply and insist on the best massage from the best instructor and rip off the strokes I liked. I called it 'nurturing massage' and put it on my card next to my phone number. And I was automatically licensed by working as an employee at the chiropractor's office. The massage therapists who shopped at the bookstore said I would now be grandfathered into the business. This was a new term to me, but once a standard practice between massage therapists and chiropractors in the trade so I could rest easy on that.

If ever I got into what I thought was a serious clinical problem, I'd either ask Dr. Galas or call the old man up on the phone at the vineyard house he was staying at in Gilroy. Our conversations on the phone lasted about all of two to three minutes. They would usually end with him saying only, "Just go back there and work on the body." So that's what I'd do. After awhile, I caught on that I didn't need to call him. If I could be alert enough, the answer would arise for me from the work itself, or from some other person or source. It could be as simple as a comment a customer would make at the bookstore.

Once there was a middle-aged woman who had a stressful job in the male corporate world and who had developed malignant cysts in her breasts. I wasn't sure what to do. I was sweating all the time trying to use my own willpower or come up with the right techniques to soothe and to secretly send her cysts away. I was at the cash register at the bookstore and overheard one woman say to another, "Do nothing." I don't remember their conversation except for that. A few days later, one of Dr. Galas's patients came in for a massage and got on the table and asked what she was supposed to do? Before I could answer, she said. "Do nothing." Now, I'd heard it twice and began to consider. When I hear things twice like this, it's time to pay attention. To hear things twice is not a linear event, with all the ducks neatly in a row, or all ribbons tied up just so, it's as if the words move in a slow spiral and return as an echo. When the middle-aged woman came in for her next massage, I ignored all the techniques and all the ideas I had been trying to get from book after book about breast cancer, and did nothing. I just worked on the body. Weeks later, she came in for her regular massage relieved and happy to report that what her doctors had diagnosed as harmful cysts, were now benign and would go away with time. I was delighted. Maybe it was a misdiagnosis, but either way, I knew on some level that I could take no credit. Mainly, I was working with people. I'd simply get out of my head and put aside any fear or uncertainty and work on the body. By doing just this, whatever problem I thought there was would invariably work out.

I'd worked so hard to become recognized in Hollywood or in New York and it was never this easy. And I remained grateful to Dr. Galas for letting me leave the mountains of details surrounding insurance and licensure alone. We kept it simple so I could stay on the job. Some body workers and massage therapists get lost in the paperwork before they ever get a good start and unfortunately give it up. These brave men and women, the kings and queens of care and comfort, don't always get the much needed support to hone and develop their craft. The planet desperately needs its massage therapists and body workers, especially now in the 21st century. It's been said by more than one wise man that whatever happens, the next twenty years from 2001 will form an energetic, signature imprint for the next thousand years to come.

One day, a month or so after I started working at the chiropractor's office, I had the distinct sense that two soft, almost electric blue hands were guiding me through the massage work I was doing. Hello? I'd often say to myself. They'd point out where to work next. I couldn't understand this and it frightened me a little bit. It was something more than I was used to and started to rock my world.

Off hours, I couldn't figure out how I could work at a store like the Bodhi Tree, of all places, the largest privately owned spiritual bookstore in the country, and be bothered by this event. I'd sold books on everything from Aurobindo to Auras, Beowulf to Behemoths, Christianity to Chakras, books I didn't always necessarily approve of, but when I was working in the back room there was no time for me to quibble. People kept feeling better and better and kept encouraging me on and I began to trust that the blue hands, as I referred to them, were beneficial and assisting and informing the work at hand. I'd just look at them point out where to work next, and say to myself, "Oh, those blue hands again, huh." They kept appearing and came even more into focus when I much later incorporated craniosacral therapy into my work. It's impossible to accurately describe this, I was just grateful they were there. I knew it was something more than my small, circumscribed "self" could accept, but if they were there, I was ready to see them. I wondered what could occur when I just worked on the body rather than get caught up in my head. It wasn't long before it seemed too trivial a matter to bring up with the old man in Northern California, besides, the words simply weren't there when I spoke with him on the phone: it was interesting, not important.

A few months later, I had the opportunity to share this with a spiritual healer I'd happened upon. She suggested I look at the pictures in a book that had just come out by a woman named Barbara Brennan called, *Hands of Light*. She cautioned me, however, not to read the book cover to cover because it could

overwhelm me with all the ideas in it. She confessed that she herself had been overwhelmed by the book, so much so that she
couldn't practice her healing for weeks, and so her suggestion was
to look at the pictures only. I took off from the office one evening,
went across the street and there it was, first edition fresh from
the press. I opened it and to my astonishment saw black and
white illustrations of soft, energetic hands guiding and working
alongside of practitioners hands in healing sessions. There were
other pages of colorful illustrations of invisible or trans-visible
"others" standing around treatment tables as practitioners worked,
and it all looked familiar to me somehow. I felt a wash of
comfort go through my body. And I was comforted about the
possibility of work with other realms, "subtle realms," realms not
immediately available to our physical senses. At least, our senses
as we know them. Were there other senses, I wondered, senses
we had to grow and develop? I shut the book closed. I'd seen
enough. More than enough. As a theater person, I'd gone about
as far as the Muses and that was just poetry. I looked around and
behind me at the few regular customers in the store, standing
vigil. Were they alone? Truly? It seemed there were others with
them. I was about to get creeped out. I abruptly left the store and
for the first time in eight years wouldn't ever have gone back
except I'd signed on for shifts the next week.

This was too much.

All throughout my shifts, I avoided those books and any
other books like them and it got me through. It's one thing to
read about experiences of others in books, another thing to have
them. Yet greater to encounter them phase by phase and in
proper sequence, without rushing ahead. Somehow I knew I was
in good hands, so to speak. I was about to be prepared to learn
how to learn. And this would take place in ways I would not have
expected in my life.

THE MOMENT BEFORE

I closed my eyes and listened to the huge sound of the ocean. I felt a thought pass through the sound. What would my life look like if I died right now? I opened my eyes, smiled. I said out loud, "Well, it would look like it does right now!" I closed my eyes again. I tried to focus. I was in my bedroom in Florida, my journal sitting quite by itself, alone.

Then something else happened a few months after I'd grown more comfortable with the blue hands. I learned to take the time and to simply sit still before beginning any session.

Sometimes I Can't Tell the Difference Between L.A .and My Mind! was really the last major performance I'd done and already it was too long ago. It had taken four years to write it, a few months to perform it and it vanished from the L.A. scene. What had I taken from it? It was about a young man named, "Freddy Madison" who had come out to L.A. from Florida in search of God and an acting career. One of his first stops is a First Baptist Church in the San Fernando Valley, where he meets with the pastor and then with a theatrical agent, but the agent hasn't seen him regularly at the church so she refuses to represent him in show business. Later, he crashes a party in Malibu to hook up with a motion picture producer, Jerry Weintraub, that one his dad's clients knows, but President George Bush—the senior—happens to be at the party and Freddy is questioned relentlessly by the FBI as to why he's pretending to be an actor! After a series of other mishaps trying to break into show business and the L.A. scene, he ends up working at a spiritual bookstore called, The Bodhi Tree. His parents visit him but his dad, who happens to be an attorney, disapproves of the Bodhi Tree, saying he smells punk — incense — in there and that the customers don't look like they have real jobs. "But they're my friends," protests Freddy. From his work in the bookstore, Freddy gets involved in a series of religions and spiritual paths, one after another after another, and finally takes a Real Estate course in San Diego. As the show opens, he is packing his things out of his apartment in UPS and FedEx boxes to go back to Florida to test for a real estate license. However, he doesn't know if in doing this, he would be selling out as an actor. He's been writing letters to God throughout the whole show, and placing them on a makeshift altar he's made to, who else? Burt Reynolds, and always trying to get an answer to find out what God's will really is for him to do, after all? Suddenly, his parents leave an urgent phone message to find out what time his plane is to arrive in where else? West Palm Beach, and he makes a hurried prayer, "Burt? Dad? I mean, God? Is it all right to talk with you? Just as a friend? I didn't mean to call you anybody else just now; I know you're not Burt Reynolds or my dad. It's just...God? I can't believe I called you Burt Reynolds! I mean, I can't believe I called you my dad! I don't know what I mean! Please will you forgive me, God? Sometimes I can't tell the difference between L.A. and My Mind...!"

I looked out the window and my eyes drifted to the odd angled stucco ceilings of my room. It was kind of a train car with a long triangle for walls. I wanted to pray to God, but would I be praying only to my dad? But I was past all that. The noise of his television was relentless. I crept down the stairs, went into my father's room, and dared to turn it down ever so low. Dad stirred in his bedcovers. I turned it up a little and scampered out into the hall, up the fourth floor stairs and back into my room.

There was nothing but the sound and salt smell of the ocean. And my journal.

What had happened? Was my life any different than "Freddy Madison's" was then? On some level, it seemed that much of the conflict with my own life story since moving to L.A. from West Palm had been cleared out of my system in the writing and performing of the one man show, and because of this, a space was made within my body, mind, and spirit for something else to happen.

But what?

I learned two very valuable lessons during the show. The first was to consider the obvious while I was onstage and the second, to be still. As to the first, I'd performed the show in small Equity Waiver theaters off Sunset Boulevard, the equivalent of Off Off Off Broadway theaters in New York, coffee houses along Melrose Avenue, the back of a bookstore now out of business in Santa Monica, the front of an art gallery on Theater Row in Hollywood, and in all cases, I had to acknowledge the actual performance space around me as it was, and not pretend it was some grand theater. However, there was one night where I actually performed it at the Burt Reynolds Dinner Theater in Jupiter, Florida with my parents and all of their friends in attendance. I doubt I could have pulled this show off had not Ms. Julie Harris, considered by the New York Times as the First Lady of the American stage, come to see the show one night in Los Angeles. That night it was in the art gallery. She was one in an audience of all about five people and about fifteen feet away from me and I realized I was nervous. I had so wanted to please her. This had to be obvious in what I was actually doing onstage, in my actions, but I didn't quite get it. My mind kept racing to the next line and it was hard to concentrate on the line I was saying. I felt out of the flow of the performance and burdened with the weight of mental details, backstage cues, ideals and ideas. The result was I began to go very quickly through every scene of the show and couldn't keep it in the moment. I started to act, in other words. And as the acting teacher, Eric Morris, said with only the title of his now classic book, "No Acting Please."

What was the way around this?

There is an ancient exercise in the Middle Eastern teaching tradition known as Sufism, where a student or disciple is asked to repeat the same task over and over again. The task could be drawing water from a well, mixing inks, or combing wool. The student doesn't know that the point of the exercise is to do the task in such a way that each moment is fresh and new. When the student catches on to the point of the exercise and can draw the water or comb the wool or lay the brick moment by moment, as if he or she has never done this before, then the student is graduated to the next level of teaching. This exercise is not so different from an actor repeating the same lines every night on stage, or from a massage therapist going through the same strokes or moves with each new person, day after day. What can keep the repetition from being mechanical, flat, and dead? The answer is to be found in the feeling of oceanic presence, of open and unconditioned space, space without boundaries that can arise for all of us from simply being still. When contact is first made with this feeling of presence at the beginning of any action, then there is communion and response. When I can learn to sit in the moment before performing any action, then there emerges a resonance of presence within and around all that is to follow. The moment before sets the tone.

"DEATH OF A SALESMAN"

Afterwards, Julie told me she loved the show and that it was wonderful, but I wasn't sure. My attention that night had been focused on what Julie, and others, would think or say about my performance rather than on the performance itself. I was sure she'd caught me "acting," but was gracious enough that evening not to point it out. Julie and I had acted in a show together in South Florida and had been pen pals and friends ever since.

The show was Arthur Miller's *Death of a Salesman,* and it was a huge personal success for me at the Burt Reynolds Dinner Theater, a black and red carpeted Mojave Desert of tables and dark leather chairs all filled with waiters and waitress rolling carts like tumbleweeds, every show. All year, I and other apprentices had been doing everything from building sets for musicals like *Little Mary Sunshine* and *Oklahoma!* to hanging lights on higher than hundred foot ladders to sewing costumes, mowing lawns and none of us were accorded the credit as actors and actresses we thought we each deserved as our God given right.

And the rights began to slip farther away from us whenever Burt Reynolds would come to visit. He'd stopped in a few times during the course of our laborious year to say hello. His hair was shaved short and he wore shiny black boots with tall heels that made him a head taller than anyone else. It was something about his height, I guess, he was shorter than most people suspected he was when on the silver screen in such movies as, *The Longest Yard, Smokey and the Bandit, Gator.* We'd file up the backstage stairs into

the wide rehearsal hall and sit down on a long row of movie theater type seats to await his arrival. His entrance would then be
announced, after several nail biting days, and he would enter alone
like Donald Trump in *The Apprentice* and take a single hard chair
on the wooden floor to face us. Then a cocktail waiter or waitress would appear from the bar downstairs, Burt's Brass Rail, and
serve him up a bottle of cranberry juice in a silver decanter with
crushed ice. We each wanted to become stars, or thought we did,
and thought that our future happiness was dependent on his
helping us there. He would then speak in a low and easy voice
about his life and how hard it was to make it in the movies and
how we couldn't depend on him for his help, but that he respected us and loved us all.

I thought he was God. But I didn't know it until writing that
prayer in my one man show. I had discovered that story running
me around and saw it and it cleared out of my body, just how I
didn't really know. Burt had been to our house when I was in my
teens and had dated my eldest sister when they were both in high
school together at Palm Beach High in West Palm Beach. He wanted to marry her and he would play and wrestle with us kids to
get on our good side. And my sister was quite beautiful and will-
ing, but Dad always disapproved of Burt because Burt was an actor and couldn't be relied upon for a steady income. It was their
dream, Burt and my eldest sister's, to someday build a theater in
Florida where actors and actresses could hone their craft before
going to New York or L.A.. Their relationship had long since ended, but now that the theater was built. Knowing this peculiar fact
made my passion in his worship that much more intense. After
a year of slave labor at seventy five dollars a week, acting in bit
parts in what shows I could get cast in, and on the brighter side,
after a year of acting classes taught by the incomparable Charles
Nelson Reilly and other stars in the Rehearsal Hall, such as Dom

DeLuise and Dolly Parton, *Death of a Salesman* was my claim to fame. Burt even had the waiters and waitresses clear the plates and stop serving drinks during the run of the show. Everybody had to go to Burt's Brass Rail during intermission.

Julie played Linda Loman and the part of Willy was played by Vincent Gardenia, who said that Willy was the role he was born to play. Years later, when Vincent passed away, I had the privilege to attend his Memorial Service in L.A. at the Improv on Melrose. Vincent is best known for his roles as the stocky Detective in *Deathwish* with the fogged eyeglasses and constant handkerchief for his nagging cold, and as Cher's wayward Italian father in *Moonstruck*. He was a dyed in the wool Brooklyner, and there were crusty character actors and comedians, some greats, and on the Improv's dark stage was a human sized black and white photograph of Vincent being comforted by Julie in the roles of Willy and Linda Loman. Julie maintains there never was a production as fine since the original with Lee J. Cobb, and the show struck a rash of Salesman revivals on and off Broadway. Julie, traditionally, holds a soft and loving radiance and is perhaps best known to movie audience as the innocent schoolgirl in *East of Eden* with James Dean and the tormented, wallflower of a heroine in *The Haunting*. She has light hair and penetrating eyes and a way about her that can, on cue, resonate straight through your bone marrow. The very atmosphere of the production could only be described as holy. It was an expression of "Holy Theater," a phrase coined by then Royal Shakespeare Company director, Peter Brook.

Vincent or Julie, by their connection to the fullness of presence, could stop a seasoned actor in his tracks all the way across stage with a look or flutter of hand. There's a space in this quality of holy theater, a shared space, where the invisible is made visible and anything can happen. It arises altogether out of the

cauldron of creation, as a whole, and on closing night, gone
forever. The play was directed and the space held, one might say,
by Ms. Harris's very close friend and confidant, Charles Nelson
Reilly. Charles brought not only his endless sense of humor but
his considerable skill in Opera and added a dream-like, Japanese
flute player to the cast who would appear and disappear at key
intervals. When things got tough backstage and jealousies loomed
among the younger actors and actresses, Charles would shout
with his baseball cap over his face, revealing his bald spot, and
his shirt falling out the front of his baggy shorts, EVERYBODY
IS FINE AND EVERYTHING IS ALL RIGHT! I was, of course,
a mere apprentice at the theater and had the privilege to be giv-
en the role of Happy, the younger son who feels hurt by his brother Biff's success in the world and who is in need of his Dad's approval on almost everything. It seemed the perfect role for me,
then, and somehow was instructive in my shaping myself into the
character of Freddy Madison later on. Julie, Vincent, and also
Charles, had met my parents at the theater and had been to our
house in Palm Beach during the run of the show. Vince would
cook pasta for us all and my sisters would sing Mom's Gershwin-
like songs and Julie and my parents grew to love each other and
stay in close touch. What I learned from the performance in the
Art Gallery that night, with five people in the audience, so many
years since my greatest achievement to date as an actor, was to
sit and take the time before going on stage.

This was all.

When an actor takes the time and becomes still in the moments before the curtain opens, then something happens. What
I mean is that something greater begins to move and express
through the actor. This is a force and expresses within the present
moment. The present moment, unlike the back and forth of the
past or the future, is open and filled with life and infinite possi-

bility. "I dwell in possibility," says the poet, Emily Dickinson. What might it be to take a moment before? It's not so dissimilar to watching how an Olympic diver takes the time before the dive itself. When the diver finally catapults off the diving board, it's as if on the wings of angels. Call it a "higher power," as they do in AA, or call it Grace, or Spirit, or Life, or the fullness of Presence. When we take the time, we acquire a force much greater than ourselves. When in presence, we are moving faster than the speed of thought.

Julie calls this shift in gear from the details and busyness of living to the vastness of the moments before and during performance, as taking on "the climate of the character." It is as if we become a force of nature. When we rush into something, into an action, there is much that we miss, but when we take our time in the moment before, just like an Olympic diver, or a great performer, we drop into a deeper level of awareness. This deeper level supports every detail of the action and almost without effort on our part. When we take a moment to be in presence, just as an actor would sit before going on stage, or the Sufi or Buddhist disciple before drawing water from the well, we find ourselves transported into an atmosphere where anything becomes possible. We are no longer "acting." We are being. We are human "Being." Alive. And authentic performance, like great massage therapy and bodywork, lives and breathes in the present moment.

I hadn't yet had any formal training in massage and bodywork and very quickly learned I had no choice, but to be still in the moments before each session began. I felt supported by my previous acting teachers and the value of concentration and working for long periods in silence. Even spiritual work is impossible without the ability to concentrate. Often people wonder if manual therapies such as massage, chiropractic, or craniosacral are safe, and it finally comes down to your practitioner and where they are at. Even skilled surgeons, if in a hurry, can be unsafe.

I learned that if I was still in the flow of moments before, during and after the sessions that the work would be more effective and even safer. It worked. I took solace in the scriptural text, "Be still and know." If I wasn't still, I found I could get caught in the details of the chiropractic office or scheduling, or in the details of the patient's diagnosis and the moment of opportunity lost. I wouldn't have showed up or been available for the patient or client and missed much. It would have been like being invited to someone's home or apartment and ignoring the host. Because I would bother to stop and to take the time, I learned to approach the human body much like a visit to someone's home or apartment. I don't barge into the door but wait until invited, once invited in, I don't raid the icebox or move the furniture around or paint the walls with my name. I like to be, what to me, is a good guest. I got this from the Old Man. I don't know what it is for you, or anyone else, to be a good guest. I can only know what it is for me to be a good guest.

This was not the behavior of a Willy Loman.

LEARNING COMMON SENSE?

I took my production copy of *Death of a Salesman* off the bookshelf in my room. The pages showed use but had yellowed with salt air and age. There were pencil markings and underlines with the character of Happy marked in faded yellow highlighter. I felt my body breathe out a breath. In fifteen or twenty years the pages might be too delicate to touch. What had happened? The show in all its magnificence had appeared out of nowhere, like a human life, taken its time on the stage, vanished. The set pieces we worked so hard to build and to make historically accurate were torn down and put into the dumpster behind the theater and workshop, never to be witnessed by any audience again. Later, I began to feel it was like a session, the way it appears, lives, and then fades. Both theater and the sessions I performed had this same quality of impermanence. Because Arthur Miller refused to see the show, it wasn't recorded, and who would ever know of it and the few lives that were quietly changed in the watching of it? I opened to Linda's compelling lines about her husband, Willy, and read, "Attention, attention must be paid."

What did she mean by the word, attention? I wondered, not for the first time. What was it to pay attention, truly, to attend?

One day, not too many months after I'd taken on the practice of being still before each bodywork and massage session, I noticed from the corner of my eye another one in the treatment room with me. It was as if there was another there who was guiding the treatments, but invisible to the naked eye. I blinked. I couldn't understand it. Then I realized I had been seeing this other one for quite some time, but that it hadn't registered in my brain. The feeling of it was that it was beneficial like the soft electric blue hands that continued to inform the work in front of me. That was the feeling of it, not the fear that tried to explain it away. Later, I thought that somehow they must be related. Over the following months, the image of this other one would appear and disappear and I couldn't understand why. It had to do with the quality of attention, almost a second attention.

I later realized I could only see or perceive this other one when I was working from a place of being still, from a place of being in presence. If I was working too fast or trying to get the work done, I'd miss it. I never mentioned it to anyone as I didn't know what it was. I didn't think it would exactly inspire the chiropractic patients I was working on and it really wasn't anyone's business. And I couldn't forget the illustrations in the Brennan book, *Hands of Light.* I guess I'd had a bad attitude toward it. I tried again and again to rationalize it away. I had no idea that this was a day in the life of those sensitized to work in the manual healing arts. I was a playwright. It bothered me, even after my years of exposure to Southern California and such new age stores as the Bodhi Tree. It seemed the point was to see it, graciously acknowledge it, and go beyond the fascination. See beyond the phenomena. To get through the day, I would look for the common sense explanation, and when anything "metaphysical" like this would show up, I'd consider the physical explanation. I'd consider what was obvious, first, and what was right in front of me to do. It worked out great. I was learning common sense and that common sense is part of the path too.

THE THIRD

Several years later, I was somewhat comforted to hear an author and educator at the bookstore, Roger Weir, tell a story of a group of early explorers in Antarctica who reported a similar event and it appealed to the rational and logical side of me. I had wandered into the large meeting room to drop off some massage brochures. There were only five or six people seated in flimsy white patio chairs and a camera was set up to tape this gentleman's talk. After a few minutes, it seemed to me this stout, well dressed, and gentle spoken man had read about every book in the world and that this was his style of "yoga," so to speak. He mentioned he'd been giving these talks every Saturday morning in L.A., without a break, for the past 26 years! Today it was a story about the Admiral Scott expedition. These were tough Edwardian explorers in competition with the great Antarctic explorer, Shackelton, and who would determine to go it on their own. Their goal was to reach the South Pole before anyone else in the Empire and they succeeded in this. However, they had not thought to bring sled dogs along with them for the return trip. Their bodies were found eight months later during the summer thaw. Each of them had kept a journal which they had written independently of the others and without corroboration, and each of the journals referred to an invisible "Third" that accompanied them in their attempt to get back home, a Third which comforted each of them in their trial.

I remembered T.S. Eliot. I turned to the bookshelf above my desk and took down a worn college copy of T.S. Eliot's, *The Complete Poems and Plays* and looked up a favorite passage from *The Waste Land:*

> Who is the third that walks always beside you?
> When I count, there are only you and I together
> But when I look ahead up the white road
> There is always another walking beside you
> Gilding wrapped in a brown mantle, hooded
> I do not know whether a man or a woman
> —But who is that on the other side of you?

Indeed, in the footnotes to *The Waste Land,* Eliot writes that this passage was inspired by the members of an Antarctic expedition and what they experienced in their plight!

It greatly comforted me.

Someone like the Medical Intuitive, Carolyn Myss might refer to this as the angel at your side. It's a common occurrence in the healing arts. I didn't know. I'd heard of this but didn't know about it in my own experience, and again, there's a huge difference between what we hear or read about and what we come to know to be true by our own experience. It opened my mind to the possibility that there may be an unseen and invisible world that gives us nurturance and assistance and which exists side by side with the world visible to the naked eye. It could be this other unseen world surrounds us, but we can't see or perceive it because our brains are too full of logic and reason or too occupied with the clamor of daily life. Upledger uses the example of the range of hearing of a dog. The sounds exist, but we can't hear them like a dog can because we don't have that bandwidth. On the other hand, maybe we all do have it, but don't use it.

I admit it's quite a lot to grasp since we are only taught to use a small portion of what we are sensorally capable of as human beings. As another example, Weir describes the full spectra of light, visible and invisible, as a rolled-up newspaper and what we can see, or think we can only see, is the width of the rubber band. I'd read about the events I was experiencing in books that I'd sold, seen it in the movies around town, heard of it around campfires at night, even at Sunday School when growing up, yet none of this had the resonance and weight of an experienced truth. Things like this simply were not supposed to happen, not in real life.

Could it be that I had a spiritual guide? I'd never asked to have one, not that I knew. How could I have one now? Weren't "spiritual guides" supposed to be dead people? I guessed there was a lot more to this world that I didn't know about. I felt giddy with the prospect, then let it go. There was work to be done and I couldn't let the joy of it get in my way.

JOY OF A SNAIL

One night, around this most bewildering time, I took my laundry basket out to the machines across the street from the upstairs bungalow where I lived off Melrose Avenue. A sensor light flashed on the walkway out front, as is typical in Hollywood, and there was this snail. It was way out of its shell and its body was wound around this leaf on top of a row of bushes. I'd seen snails on the sidewalks and felt so bad when I'd step on them in a rush. It was late and I was tired, but I stopped to look. I looked at the trees out on the sidewalk and back at the snail. It served me right. A few days before I had shown a client how to hug a tree! It wasn't just any tree, of course, it was one of the trees along Westmount, an avenue that ran alongside the office. It was most strange. I approached the tree as if it were a craniosacral client and imparted to it a very light touch. In moments, the tree seemed to wake up underneath my fingertips. I moved a little bit closer to it, trying to avoid the classic "hug." I wondered if it had a lymph system, and how it circulated water? It certainly did not have a craniosacral system! I mused upon these things and then noticed, from the corner of my eye, that all the trees on the street, of the same kind, appeared to wake up. It was as if each tree of the same family virtually glowed. My client was a saxophone player and familiar with playing in large bands. I told him to check it out using a very light touch. Then I suggested he raise his vision to include the other trees. "They're glowing," he said. "They like this." His words. I wasn't sure who was crazier, him or me.

And now I was faced with a snail. I looked closer. It seemed to me to move with a certain joy of movement on this leaf. I put my free hand out. Could I somehow tune in with the snail and feel its warmth and joy? It was just a snail and a little less round than my baby finger. It reached so far out of its delicate brown shell toward my hand I thought it would lose its home. I wondered, had I ever felt such joy in a simple leaf? It could have been nothing else than joy. Its tiny neck unwound into a yoga posture that only a snail could do and became still. I sensed an energy blockage just like a little cyst of energy below the snail's right horn. I magnetized my finger to it and slowly pulled it out. I sent the tiny blockage away into the air to wherever such things go. The snail turned and stretched into another tiny yoga posture that could only be called the "snail," then, it appeared to look at me with its dark eyes. It was like its whole body smiled. I looked to see if anyone else was around. No one had seen me, and I let my own body smile with the joy of a snail. Then I had a sense of another, of the Third beside me, and wondered if somehow in that moment, I was like a "third" to that snail. I went directly to the laundry machines and tried to forget about it.

SKULL BONES MOVE?

Osteopathy? I thought of the Healthplex Clinic and all the faces there. I'd first heard of this healing art in California, and couldn't even pronounce it. I called it the "unpronounceable therapy."

Over the years I'd learned that massage therapy was a doorway into other forms of healing arts. Often Massage Therapists graduate from their practices and go to medical school, chiropractic, acupuncture, or Traditional Chinese Medicine, even osteopathic college. For me, it seemed it would be this little known form of healing art. I'd learned about aspects of it here and there around town and began to incorporate aspects of it as a blend into my bodywork and massage therapy. When the bones of people's skulls began to move under the slightest touch, I seriously considered formal training for the first time so I could work considerately and harmlessly with others.

I was beginning a massage with a sophisticated, middle-aged woman I'd never met before who was suffering from cluster headaches. It was my job to give her a full body massage and relax the sore muscles in her legs and shoulders in preparation for a treatment with the chiropractor. My fingers gently soothed her cheeks and then moved to her forehead and very lightly held and caressed her there for a few moments.

Then my hands became still.

After a while, I wondered what my hands were doing on her forehead for so long but she didn't seem to mind or say anything aloud. It seemed a nice enough opening gesture. I began to feel a little sleepy. I looked at the clock on the shelf above my table. Then I felt her entire forehead move as if by itself. I backed off. I really didn't know what had happened. I'd by now worked for three years in this same back room without training, and curiosity got the best of me. I placed my hands on her forehead once more and then it shifted again.

"Whoa," I whispered.

I didn't know what I had done and was suddenly alarmed. It felt as if the entire bone of her forehead had lifted off and away from the rest of her face and into the air. Thankfully, she gave a very deep sigh of relief. I quickly moved away from her head and to her feet. I had no conception of what had just happened. I rubbed some lotion into my palms and placed my hands around her insoles and stretched her ankles when she said, with great delight, "My headache's gone away."

"Uhm. Wonderful," I answered.

I felt unnerved. What had I done?

A space had opened in this woman where before there was contraction and it was most effortless.

It seemed just as the earth has tectonic plates that can move and are connected to the core of the earth, the bones of the skull can move and are somehow connected to a core, the core of the body. And just as the earth is composed of mostly water and fluid, so is the human body about seventy-eight percent water in the average adult. I could only touch this fluid environment in stillness and presence. And it would lovingly respond. Again and again it was one thing to read about or see on a video, another thing to experience under my hands.

I searched the Bodhi Tree for any books on this phenomenon and a magazine fell from the shelf on the wooden floor — we never shelved the books and magazines very well. When I went to pick it up, the magazine had opened to a black and white page with the word, "Trust." It was just an advertisement but for something called craniosacral therapy. I was enthused to discover that a key place of adjustment in craniosacral was at the atlas and the axis, and this began my interest in craniosacral therapy in earnest. But I never had a chance to check in with the old man in Northern California about it — the words would vanish from me even on the phone. I could not know that someday I would encounter dolphins as a treatment approach and that when I would place hands on clients, using only a very light touch, it would often feel like placing hands on the surface of intelligent water. Maybe it wasn't all that important. Interesting, yes, not important. So I just kept the mood up and the tone high, as he'd say, and went about my business working on the body.

Maybe I shouldn't say this again, but it wasn't as if I had become immune from fear. I'd had no formal training, and now, it seemed clients' skull bones were moving under the slightest touch. I had a lot I could be afraid about, if I went there. I also had resistance to formal training, not that training wouldn't be just what the Doctor ordered. Around this time, a massage therapist friend told me over coffee at the Urth Café, just across from the office, that lately, she'd been feeling fearful. She told me there were times when she would imagine that Secret Service and FBI agents — "Men in Black" — were watching her every move. It was as if they were behind the walls or checking in on her in her own private bathroom. I looked back and around the Urth Café's outdoor tables, dramatically, as if we were both being watched. She slapped my wrist, "I'm not kidding!"

Later, I realized that I still had some impressions of fear too. I remembered how I'd once read a simple book by the same, J. Krishnamurti, entitled, *The Flame of Attention.* I'd never sat to read a book by this fine old gentleman cover-to-cover, but one of my UCLA Extension poetry teachers had suggested our class read it. I dove into it in the food court of a shopping mall in LA., and because it spoke the truth, soon it was as if Secret Service Agents and CIA were monitoring my every thought as I read each word. After all, I was stepping out beyond the societal agreement, the *consensus,* that I should never question authority and always obey and do what "I'm" told by my "betters." My betters who only want to "help" me to always do the right thing—whatever that is, exactly. Now, with my involvement in hands-on healing, I should have known that electric blue hands, an invisible world, even Angels, could not exist. Not to mention the longstanding societal agreement, at least in this country, that the human head is fused like a bowling ball after infancy and that the skull bones cannot move! I really appreciated my friend's telling me her fears and bringing my own fears to my attention. In my off hours, I too would experience qualities and shades of fearful imagery that would threaten to stop the creativity in working on the body and even the expansion in consciousness. At the end of the day, and at the beginning of the day, it's easy to forget that, *I am in charge of my inner state of being.* The images could be as whacky as my doing horrible things to others just by my thoughts, FBI Agents, hooded Gangbangers, Lions, Tigers, and Bears. Oh, my!

With the help of the old man's taped talks, I would learn to recognize this as a typical trap when one was about to make a break through into another, expanded level of consciousness. The sense of being watched or impending doom, and so on, has no basis in reality, but was only the image making ability of the mind. It can be any image or series of images, from personal health to natural disaster. I didn't feel ashamed of leaning on yet another person's books and tapes. However evolved we are, or think we are, sometimes a different point of view is needed. It's the image making ability of the mind that we really fear, he'd said. When we can observe our own ability to come up with such wild and outlandish images, even the fear of being able to come up with such images in the first place, we are watching and on the way to wakefulness. We can be put to sleep by any kind of fearful imagery, even from the Evening News, and if we are to remain on the job, we are required to stay awake. Being awake or asleep depends on our being responsible or not responsible for the images in the mind. When we can take responsibility for making these images, even those made by raw emotions, by freely experiencing them, we are on the way to the proper use of the mind and to a greater expansion and expression in living. Despite my resistance to formal training, I began to welcome any fearful imagery that might arise from the image making ability of the mind. I would actually look forward to it, as if I were looking forward to watching a game or movie. Why? Now I knew when such fearsome impressions would appear, from within or without, it meant I was about to open into another level of consciousness and of change, a fresh and a new level of being, if not to the present moment.

(What is fear but lack of trust?)

IN A VINEYARD WITH MOM

A couple years into my new career, long before I would go to massage school, I drove my mom up the California coast so she could meet this old man for herself. I'd picked her up at LAX and it was just the two of us. She remembered the time she was here before, when it was with Dad and me, but this time, our route wasn't the coast but through the great San Joaquin Valley on the I-5. She was dressed in bright red silk slacks and a beige leather coat with her hair up in a paisley scarf. The bright blue, red, and gold of her costume jewelry on her fingers and neck glistened in the sunlight that poured in through the windows of my leaky Honda. She talked a mile a minute about everything and wanted to know everything about me and my acting career but there wasn't much to say.

"Now, you talk, I'll listen," she'd say.

And that's about how it went. The plan was to visit with the old man and then for me to take her up to Placerville, "Gold Country," where she would visit for two months with one of my sisters while Dad and I went to the Amazon and Macchu Picchu. Macchu Picchu, unlike the Buddhists, was Dad's idea. Neither Dad nor I knew what to expect and this overweight Hispanic guide in a khaki flak suit had kept showing up at Dad's office for more cash to build a balsa wood raft for the Amazon and two five-hundred horsepower Evinrude engines to steer it. I don't know why Dad wanted to go and I tried to talk him out of it because the whole idea freaked me out but he wouldn't hear of it.

Our route would take us through the Peruvian Amazon on a raft and then high in the Andes and the city of Cusco, which Dad really wanted to see, and I guess it reminded him of our trips with the Indian Guides but I'm still in the middle of processing the trip so that's another story. It can take me awhile to process each trip I take out of the country. This is so I can learn something, which to me makes the whole trip worthwhile and not just another vacation. Mom had heard from me that the old man smoked cigarettes and ventured to ask me for a Tareyton as we bounced north beyond the Grapevine on I-5. I laughed and said, "No way." She took out pair of sleek black leather gloves from her Louis Vuitton purse, put them on, and said, "Now, I'm ready."

I handed her a cigarette from the pack in my top pocket. When she used that definitive tone of voice there was no refusing. She put it between her teeth and I tried to help her light it with my lighter but we ended up using the cigarette lighter from the car. She puffed but couldn't balance it on the edge of her lip to get the smoke going. Finally, she gave it to me. It had red lipstick smeared all over it.

"Why do you smoke?" she said. "It's a hassle."

"I find it's grounding. And pleasant."

"Pleasant? Throw out those coffin nails this minute!"

"Mom?"

"Okay, you talk, I'll listen."

Someone had given him a different place to live in, but it was still at the vineyard. Instead of the main house, he was in the back in a full size trailer home. We pulled up on the gravel driveway going about four miles per hour. There were fragrant roses planted at each of the vine rows and each row marked by its grape or blend: cabernet, pinot noir, chardonnay. There is something special about the atmosphere of that vineyard in the "garlic capital of the world." The Hispanics who work there say it's because the old man blessed the vineyard. When that wine is tasted, flavor almost becomes irrelevant due to the life held within the wine itself. This is not to say that the flavor isn't exquisite, but the ground is cared for by hand and with loving intention and what emerges from that soil is the essence of the grape. It's uncanny, but the difference between that wine is as day to night with the larger house wines of Northern California. Maybe it's just me.

The great ponderosa pines and eucalyptus trees were fragrant with the warmth of the day and delphiniums, pansies, and roses blossomed everywhere. We passed the main house, curved around toward the back and looked for where to go. When I saw him move inside the window, I hoped Mom wouldn't mind he was in a trailer. "It's not the container, it's the contents," I whispered aloud. The old man had worked hard to keep any attention away from him as a personality. She looked at me and nodded, then gave an expectant smile. I'd shared one or two of his talks with her on my boom box on a visit back home. We'd heard his talks on the sun deck, which spans the length of the Florida room and overlooks the ocean, the same deck where we used to paint oil canvases together of the ocean when I was but a child. He stepped out the front door and greeted us from the raised wooden porch in a tan sports coat with the top button missing. I slowed down the Honda even more, held my breath, and went to the other side to help Mom out. He didn't seem to smile but in his soft southern drawl, invited us to come up the steps and sit on the white, plastic lawn chairs. I was wondering if I'd said anything wrong, but we hadn't spoken yet. He appeared a lot older than I remembered him, his hair seemed more gray than snowy white and there was kind of limp at his instep which seemed to be a minor annoyance for him.

"So you made it up the stairs all right? Good."

We didn't go inside. He held each of my mother's feet and hands, one after the other. In the warmth and glow of his presence, there was a growing familiarity between them, as if they were old friends. I wondered if they were close in age and of the same generation. Now, she'd developed diabetes and I was worried for her and wanted him to save her. It was only for a few minutes, but she went on a high for weeks and said he was a Prophet. This was a lot for my mother to say since she had raised all of us as Southern Baptists. My mom is from a line of Baptist ministers who left from New York State and settled in South Florida at the beginning of the last century. After what seemed only a few minutes but was much longer, he took his hands off her feet and said, "There you are, precious one." There was a light in her eyes and a joy of being I hadn't seen in a long time. She wrote him out a two hundred and fifty dollar check, more than I ever thought possible you could ever give anyone for doing just that, and we made our goodbyes.

Who was this man? What was he? Perhaps he really was a Prophet, I thought now, but a modern day Prophet, a true man of God, a man who had long ago fathomed the inner meaning of the Bible, and its mysteries, and yet managed to remain hidden, aloof, from all fanfare, all institutions. He could have become rich and powerful, known for a thousand years, but he'd always said, it's the contents that count, not the container. The memory of this man would soon dissolve away with the waters of time, not his teaching. And what of his teaching? Perhaps it would take on a different form, somewhere else on the planet, and remain as quiet and unheralded.

My thoughts started to churn when away from his presence, and I'd wanted to ask him what he did because he didn't seem to use any techniques. He just held her sore feet and hands. How could it be possible to do so much good for another without using any techniques? "He didn't really do anything," I said. "Did he?" She didn't seem to hear, unusual for her when I spoke out loud. I drove with her through the lake country back to the upper San Joaquin Valley and dropped her off at my sister's home near the town of Placerville. She was ecstatic. We sang some of the Gershwin-like songs she'd written that our whole family knew the words to and snapped our fingers. I'd used this one song we sang in my one man show and it starts with a happy piano tune and it goes something like this:

> My! What a wonderful world!
> Yes, what a beautiful world,
> If you make it that way — !
>
> Hey, all the people are nice,
> They'll shake your hand even twice,
> If you make it that way —!
>
> You can go crrrrazy! Any day of the week,
> If you worry 'bout what folks think,
> 'Cause Folks aren't thinkin'
> What you think they are thinkin' —
>
> My! Hey, what a wonderful world!
> Yes, what a beautiful world,
> If you make it, make it, make it,
> If you make it, make it, make it,
> If you maaaaake it, that way — !

Then I drove back to Los Angeles, and from there, I flew on to Miami where I met my dad for our trip to the Amazon and Macchu Picchu. That was in 1992. My mother and the old man would both pass on two years later in 1994, two weeks apart from each other. Both of them were seventy-eight. Both from diabetes. It devastated me.

OUR HOME HAS A HEALING

My mother and the old man were great supporters of anything I set my mind on to do. My father was also devastated and broken hearted and I couldn't draw on him for strength and encouragement. I felt particularly disoriented after the passing of the old man as I'd always felt very confident in bucking the system with him around and with him easily available on the phone. And then there was this new art I was encountering that I couldn't talk with anyone about. Facial bones were moving underneath my hands. I needed proper training and soon.

Three days after his passing I saw him again. I didn't mention this event to anyone, and yet now, I didn't feel orphaned or abandoned. I was sitting out on the top of the kitchen steps which led to our driveway and saw him at the bottom of the stairs. I couldn't believe it. It was like seeing the Third that I'd been seeing in sessions for so long. He was dressed well in his old sports coat, shirt with the missing button, and long pants. He waved to me with his hand to follow him. It was dark out and I was unsure. I was in shorts and sandals with a white T-shirt. Only my dad was upstairs in his bedroom and no one else was around. So I went down the red and white painted stairs. He went ahead and motioned me to follow him out the driveway to North Lake Way, which fronted the house to the West. I did, and then he took a right turn and to the main road, North Ocean Boulevard.

The sound of the ocean started to increase in volume as I followed him up the hill to the beach, and there was a slight wind

I hadn't noticed from the back of the house. At this point he started to look toward the house. I looked too, wondering what was up? It was the same four storied white stucco house and Tudor style red gabled roof I had always known. Hedges of Australian pine, sea grape, and small cocoanut trees surrounded the house from the road. The kitchen lights were on along the side of the house, and as we rounded the curve, the flag was up but the flag pole light was off, which was unusual. Dad always saw the American and Navy flags were lit at night. There was the main house, the portion built by the Sea Captain so long ago, and the long addition of the Florida room Dad had built with the pool and pool deck out front. Dad's bedroom lights were on in the main house and above, the lights to my room, just under the wide triangular eve, but underneath our rooms, Mom's parlor was dim, and the row of fluorescent lights that spanned the Florida room were out.

The place looked peculiar without the many family members, relatives, and friends who constantly visited. The sky was dark except for a few bright clouds far out at sea. He looked again to the house and then I saw, with a second attention: My mother had passed away in the Florida room, on her request, and had been brought home from the hospital in her last few hours. There was a soft light around the main house, but at the center of the Florida room where her hospital bed had been, there was now a dark hole of grief and pain. It was as if a bomb had exploded there.

Mom had only left two weeks before. All of my sisters had gathered around her and each had been keening and grieving in their own ways. They were now mostly of middle age or approaching, dressed in business suits, shorts, pajamas. I never knew any of my sisters to have such sounds and such creativeness in their expression. And bluer eyes than I had ever seen. I realized

I didn't know them, as people. Each one had a different object or memento in their hands that they placed in a semi-circle around her head in the few minutes after she'd gone. One a small heart made of rose quartz, one a child's tiny bible, one the pink Ever Ready Bunny Rabbit. I stood back, an observer, as if of a play. It was unreal to me. I was in shock but still I could observe. Throughout the whole of that evening, I'd had a sense of the old man going from Florida room to Parlor to Kitchen giving comfort to each person that was there. It was as if he were an invited guest, and intent on paying full attention to the Host. I would follow his considered cues that fateful night and see that each person had a private time to visit with Mom in the Florida room and then accompany each back to the Parlor for the next person's turn. I thought of him for the first time like a shepherd. I didn't have to call him on the phone in California, yes, I knew he was in California at the vineyard, but he was here too.

I felt sort of a butler at a marvelous party, and soon most all the family sat in Mom's Parlor, the Blue Room, as some call it, with its fine couches, antique silk chairs, baby grand piano, light blue carpet and walls, with a warmth of good feeling, good will, and good conversation among all. We could hear mother's complaints in the Florida room. We all whispered to each other that her own mother was there now, the pastor's wife, who had long passed away. Mom was on a morphine drip, but would shout out with fury at her mother, "No mother. Go away. It's not time. Go away Mother. AWAY!"

And after it all calmed down, after she'd passed, I wondered where did all that energy go? It didn't just go nowhere. Mom had been full of "piss and vinegar." Where had it gone? It was here only moments ago. Dad sat at her side with the family Bible in his hands and my sisters gathered around the bed. We all agreed she had passed at the perfect time, for her. Dad opened the Bible and his voice cracked as he read the passage that went, "Though I walk through the Valley of the Shadow of Death...." Mom, in the same dress she wore at their 50th anniversary, flowed up behind Dad, in the midst of his grief, and touched him on the shoulder. I was sitting with one of my nephews, himself an actor, at the other side of the bed, opposite Dad. My nephew was in his twenties with brown eyes and quite the ladies man but as an actor, deep and sensitive.

"You see her?" I said.

"She's there," he said. "She's beautiful."

"Yeah."

"Why is everyone so sad?"

"Beats me," I said. "She's right there."

It was exciting for both of us to share this discovery.

We kept it a secret.

But now there was a hole, a dark hole at the center of the Florida room, like it had been hit by a bomb, and the Old Man and I could see it from the ocean road. Otherwise, a soft light around the house, a light that didn't seem to be from the streetlight standing as it always had at the edge of the curve by the beach. It was a light of a different spectra and yet almost tangible. It felt safe. Had I completely lost my mind? The old man had only passed away three days ago, two weeks after Momma. The world had felt absent without him. It was on December 18, 1994. There was a fog all that night in Los Angeles, a fog so thick and sad and un-navigable it seemed the Earth itself was mourning the loss and I had come home to be with Dad. Now, the old man lifted up his hands and directed them toward the dark hole. Taking his cue, I lifted up mine, and together we sent light and energy and warmth and love.

Then.

A cross of liquid white light appeared out from the darkness and it was of tremendous size going up to the heavens, and it was as if it had always been there but soiled over somehow, and the deep ocean behind and the few homes surrounding ours dropped away and the whole north end of that town dropped and became like a valley of angels, all flying in the outer rim of this great bowl with the cross as fulcrum and fluid center. Next, all disappeared, even the house, and there was nothing.

Then life. The house, the beach, the houses on either side all came back. It was for the time of a blink. Nothing. Then. Light. The house had taken a wound with my mother's passing, and now was healing, the rend repaired. It was only a light gray color now where it was dark before, and the grayness was crumbling like dust and fast fading away. I felt a sense of utter joy to be doing this at all with the Old Man. I didn't know that events like this were common to intuitive body workers and massage therapists and energy workers, more specifically, with any relationships of the heart. I wasn't really open to it, not in reality. I had thought, rather assumed, for most all my life when someone died, or seemed to die, that that was that and no more. And perhaps for some, this is true, not for others. After three days that seemed an eternity, it was if our relationship as friends renewed and was as before. The only disadvantage I'd have was calling him on the phone, but then I could save on long distance bills. It was fun to stand shoulder to shoulder with him on the road that night, in this glorious fantasia, out in front of our neighborhood beach cabana, and to treat the house just this way.

As I sat in my bedroom, I recalled a similar fog in Los Angeles the night of J. Krishnamurti's passing in Ojai, California, and more recently, the night one of the great Sikh teachers, Yogi Bhajan, passed in Espanola, New Mexico. For most of us a sudden fog is merely an inconvenience. Such impenetrable fogs as this only happen rarely in Los Angeles, once in many years, and are

far more rare than electrical storms there. Rather than accuse myself of being crazy, I try to remember that when I'm in such a sad
and mournful fog, it could mean that one of the earth's lovers has
gone and that many may be in grief. I may or may not know who
it was that passed at the time. I may never know this. I can only
know by the feeling of the fog. It's very subjective. It makes no
sense to the logical mind. But it's a different feeling than the wet,
pea soup fogs that appear with such regularity in San Francisco
or the Pacific Northwest, and are supposed to appear as part of
the earth's natural balancing act. It's all in the tone of the feeling
of it. For example, I'd had no connection to Yogi Bhajan and had
never met the man. I knew that he'd had thousands of followers
and admirers in the West who practiced the discipline of Yoga. I
didn't know he'd passed away. I sensed the grief within the fog
first, and only later put the two seemingly unrelated events together. For me, these are rapid feedback responses from the Earth
to personal losses among smaller groups of people in deepest grief,
and could occur quickly, within hours. Anyway, it was something
to think about, if only to entertain the question.

I didn't know houses could be "treated." Since Mom's passing there was a sense that something had been missing in the
house, something more than Mom's physical presence, and a sense
of darkness and grief. What's more, as I think back to the first days
of doing massage therapy, I'd see dark patches just over the skin
on some bodies, like a second skin, but a skin that had been rend
by the slings and arrows of outrageous fortune, the stress and
heartbreak of living, and lay hands to gently fill these holes and
patches with new energy and warmth and life. It was always
deeply soothing, calming, and comforting to the client and/or patient. All it took was to step back from the busyness of giving the
massage and take the time to let the flood of energy and warmth

fill. Taking the time is always the challenge because it's so easy to forget. Just a simple "time out" can make all the difference in another person's day.

After this healing event, the house began to take on a different atmosphere and friends and family began to visit more and spend more time there. I could not take the credit and so said nothing about it, just enjoyed the company when I was there. I felt happy because people would remark on the good feeling of the house, like they used to before Mom passed. Mom was considered an angel by all this community, and her and Dad were the first to set up the Bible study groups in the homes when this was frowned upon here. Now, it's more accepted, but people to this day comment on how good they felt and feel in this environment. It was exciting to discover that just as a human body could be healed, a house also could be healed. After this, I began to pay attention to the living environments I would enter to see if there were any "dark holes," or what the feeling was in my own body about being in different environments. In an office building or in someone's home, I would wonder if I felt comfortable and open in my body, or uneasy and tight? In the ocean out front there are areas where the water is warmer and areas where the water is cooler from the shifting flow of the tides and currents. You can be swimming in a bathtub-like warmth and suddenly enter a cool spot. There were warm and cool spots around office buildings, apartment dwellings, and homes and also around the bodies that I would regularly work on, and this would remain in the background of my attention. I came across a line of the poet, Rumi that somewhat validated my feeling about living spaces and it goes something like this: If love did not live in matter, how could any place have any hold on anyone?

And it wasn't too many days after this event that I was somehow open enough to perceive my mother during sessions in the

Florida room, mostly when doing massage or craniosacral therapy on Dad. My Dad would see her during these sessions, and say, "Momma is with me now." This amazed me really because I'd always assumed Dad was an attorney and businessman and closed to this kind of experiencing.

One afternoon, during the Holidays, I wandered into the Florida room.

MY DAD ALONE

In the late Saturday afternoon
when the football game is over and when
my sisters have left with their children,
I see my dad alone on the couch
where my mom died.
He sits there with his videos,
videos of us when we were children: working in
   the yard.
I see him now and his plans for the building of
   the blue point marble
Mausoleum
for my mom who will go there soon.
We will move her grave for her and
lift it into this second residence. I walk
into the Florida room and I stop.
I don't want to disturb him.
There is nothing in the room but presence.

It was four years after I began massage therapy, in January, 1996, that I took my first formal course in craniosacral therapy in Santa Barbara, California. Again, there are other wonderful schools of craniosacral, but I wasn't aware of them at the time.

And so after two years of study, combined with clinical practice and rigorous examinations, I received my first level of certification in craniosacral therapy. I attended anatomy and physiology courses designed for nurses at Glendale Community College in Glendale, California, but didn't like the sight of blood or being around cadavers. I was now on a roll, taking formal courses, and it seemed the next step was to either go to medical school, chiropractic school, or massage school. I didn't think of osteopathy school.

What was it about the color blue?

THE COLOR BLUE

I had turned the chair around by my writing desk to face the windows. I sat in the chair, adjusted my sits-bones on the thick corduroy cushion, and got quiet. My head had been filled with books, plays, journals. A moment later, a rush of light left my chest and I saw the old man standing a few feet away right here in my room. His hair was snowy white and his sport coat tan. It wasn't as if he was from somewhere else now. It was as if he were part of me. Or a part of a part of me. I averted my eyes and did my best to forget this ever happened and try to sit. "Be still," I said aloud. I preferred to think that he really was outside of me. It was just more fun that way.

Then.

I rushed out of my room, ran down the stairs, walked quietly down the blue carpeted hall past Dad's room, made a sharp right along the banister, down the next flight of stairs, curved around again to the right at the bottom of the stairs, ran straight through the parlor, and hopped the two steps into the pineapple decorated foyer, which made up the entrance to the Florida room, and joined the main house. I skipped into the Florida room and tattered at myself, "Virgin! Virgin! Virgin!" I don't know why. I had been thinking how, with all of my sisters, that I had been raised to marry a rich white man, just like them, and was supposed to have stayed a virgin, like most of them had before they were married. These thoughts happen when we visit our family homes. I broke into a run all the way past the curved floral couches, the souvenirs from every country in the world, Spain, France, Morocco, South America, the sparkling ceilings, past the big screen Panasonic TV, to pull the iron nail out of the sliding glass doors at the end of the room, took a sharp left outside toward the ocean, passing the pool, unbolted the dark red painted gate that fronted the house, checked for traffic, but there were no cars coming up the curve and none all the way south, then ran across the road to skip the two steps down into the cabana and raced through the loose sand path through the sea oats and sandspur bushes, kicking sand as my heels dug in, and stopped at the edge of the ocean.

"What's going on here?" I shouted.

The light was beginning to show over the eastern horizon. A few soft breakers rolled into foam and came up to meet my feet. I look out into the blue and there was nothing but me and the sea. My body calmed. There was nothing there. Just ocean and sky and the color blue. I looked north and remembered where Dad and I were today. I'd heard of the Upledger Institute in California, but it wasn't located in California. It was located in the town of Palm Beach Gardens, which is adjacent to the town of Jupiter, which is the town where I'd worked as an apprentice to earn my Actor's Equity union card. The theater itself is located across the street from a hotel resort which fronts the ocean and where the Institute holds most of its Florida courses. Not long after my certification, I took a yet another craniosacral therapy course at this very resort. It was taught by Alice Quaid, the same woman who Dad and I had met today before our session. This couldn't be important. Maybe I was still emotionally releasing or something from the session.

This happens.

During the course, I'd walked out onto a balcony of the resort which happened to overlook the theater. The once proud theater had years ago been abandoned. I looked down at the empty parking lot which surrounded the theater, at white dirt and gravel, and recalled my hopes as an actor and passionately rehearsing my lines for plays. I wondered then at the meaning of this apparent synchronicity. *Synchronicity* is a term coined by the great psychologist, Carl Jung, a contemporary of Freud, which he used for separate coincidences that are so closely related that they can become meaningful. It's a term that has come down to the popular jargon along with the phrase "meaningful coincidence." Needless to say, I was a little weirded out, especially since I'd left Florida to go out to California in search of God and an acting career. Now my path was pointing to my own backyard.

What could this mean? I still wasn't sure. I'd been in the habit of asking what synchronicities might mean when I'd had time for some contemplation. Both Institute and Theater were just a few miles north of here down the beach. Maybe it was for me, after all, to work in healing arts rather than in writing or in the theater or in the movies.

I recalled my last few days in Florida before I ever left for California. I recalled that I never would have gone to Los Angeles if I didn't have a kind of dream or vision which seemed to point the way. After I had finished my apprenticeship, I drove my old white Nova over some small sand dunes on Jupiter Island and parked under towering Australian pines. The wind started to kick up over the ocean waves and I rolled up the window and pulled the seat back and looked at the ceiling of the car. I didn't know if I should go to New York to be an actor or go to Los Angeles to be an actor. The indecision was driving me crazy and I'd already asked too many people about which place to start. I closed my eyes and fell half asleep. In my half dreaming state, I saw theaters and proscenium arches and empty stages and blank movie screens and all of which gradually filled with images, events, and light. It appeared that I was involved as an actor on these stages and on these screens, and as a writer, and somehow as a director, and that I had a starring role in these stories. I then saw, with all due respect, Jesus Christ appear from the background in a seamless white robe. He was easy and casual and smoking a cigarette.

I asked, "Could it be?"

And Jesus said, "Go to Los Angeles. There you will find the work."

I don't remember what else he said after that or if anything at all. But I said, "How will I know this is a true vision? I don't want to be deceived." I asked for a sign.

I then heard within, "Like a bolt of blue."

I opened my eyes. I looked around the interior of my Nova. No bolt of blue. I got out and stood by the ocean. The ocean is blue, I thought, but this was to be a bolt of some kind. I hunkered down on my knees. It will come to me like a bolt out of the blue, I thought. Or was it, bolt of blue? I looked for a thunderbolt for a long time. There was wind but no sign of rain. No sign. I sighed. It was plain ocean. I became depressed. I got into my car, turned on the ignition and thanked Jesus, anyway. I drove over the loose sand to the road.

Less than an hour later, I pulled up to a gift shop owned and managed by a kindly woman who I'd been renting a room from and liked very much. Her store had cards, teas, candles, and spiritual books and was called, *Sisters of the Sun*. She couldn't talk with me as there were customers so I picked up a book off the shelf. It had an orange cover with a strange man on the front. He had dark feminine eyes. The book was called *Autobiography of a Yogi* and written by a great hearted yogi Paramahansa Yogananda, who had traveled from India to Southern California in the 1940's. I had seen this book before in my early teens at a new age bookstore in West Palm Beach called "The Rainbow Bridge," which I'd gone into with my mother. It was a block or so away from the First Baptist Church of West Palm Beach and Mom and I were on an adventure. It was the first new age or "spiritual" bookstore — I never know what to call these things — that I'd ever set foot into and it was a change from the rarified airs of Palm Beach with its cocktail parties and debutante balls. The book I bought that day when I was 15 was by J. Krishnamurti, who talked about the difference between the phony and the real. My life felt anything but real. Any struggle to become a somebody, or a something, was shallow, he said. The shallow are always afraid of what they are. Then I looked at a hippie poster on the wall with some odd shaped writing. It was written in Sanskrit and from an ancient text called the Upanishads.

> From the unreal lead me to the Real
> From darkness lead me to Light,
> From death lead me to Immortality.

In the decades and years that followed I'd gotten caught up in this struggle toward trying to achieve immortality as a writer and actor. Maybe I was into a different quality of immortality than the applause of men, all along, and just forgot? Now, I looked at the other colorful shelves in my friend's gift shop. I felt strangely compelled to the book by this man with the soft eyes, not knowing who he was, Yogananda. She didn't have the J. Krishnamurti book. It would have to be Yogananda. Anyway, it was just a book.

The page I opened to described how in India all of life is called Maya, or illusion, and how we are all writers, actors, and directors of our own motion pictures. My eyes widened. He said that whenever he would watch a movie and be disturbed by the imagery, all he would do is remember to look up to see the light from the projector flashing above his head. It's all a motion picture dream, he said, and we each are the stars of our own stories. We all play our roles. I turned the page. And there, a small blue flower. I looked again. I reread the pages. The flower had a delicate stem and five petals. It looked like a star. I was astonished.

My friend asked, "What's going on?" I picked up the flower and tried to talk through my excitement about what was happening. She tried to follow what I was saying, and then I thought, this is just an ordinary flower.

"It's just a flower," I said.

She said, "Never underestimate the power of a little blue flower."

Years later, after increasing disappointments in my acting and playwriting career, I told my mother about it. I said again, "It was just a flower."

My mother said, "No. I've seen that variety of flower in every country I've traveled in the world. It's everywhere. It gathers in bushes even on the highways. That means something. Find out."

What could this mean? There I'd been on the balcony which overlooked the abandoned theater, just a few miles north of here. The moral of this story could be that anyone can ask for a sign from the heavens, but can anyone interpret it correctly when it is given? For years I had assumed the blue flower had meant good fortune in theater, in acting and in playwrighting, but it could have meant something else entirely. I began to recall something else I'd been seeing during sessions. When I first saw this event occur, it was as if I saw it from the corner of my eye. If I'd blinked it would have gone away. It wasn't anything I could do, of myself, it simply occurred. I still didn't give it much thought, but now brought it back into sharp focus. I had for a long time during treatment sessions perceived a luminous line of blue which would appear at the base of the spine, at the sacrum, and travel up through the core of the body and into the cranium where it would open and blossom above the forehead like a luminescent blue flower. I'd been scribbling it down in my case notes calling it the line of harmony. I had no other words for it. I felt sure this is what most of the experts in the craniosacral trade knew about, but which no one would talk about, and for good reason. It's so delicate; we can't know it with trying to know it. And then there was something about the dolphins. I didn't know if I'd ever know.

I curled my toes over the wet sand and turned my head to the house. It cut quite a silhouette beyond the patches of sea oats and tiny dunes. I stepped back and looked at the ocean. "Hi dolphins, I know you're out there now. Hello?"

I could have almost jumped in after them.

"Hello," I said again.

Then I thought of all the show offs I'd come across in all fields, healing art and theater art, and wondered if I was a show off for even thinking these thoughts? To show off is to be phony, isn't it? It's to miss the mark. We become filled with lies about ourselves and then can do nothing really; we have lost and are then, less than a human being. What set me on the path long ago was to go from the unreal to the real. I needed no more of pride parading as self esteem. This was nothing in the blue flower to pretend or show off about, this was a mystery that could never be explained or put into words. It was a grace. There were times when the flower's opening and blossoming through the deep core had been accompanied by a full and satisfying feeling throughout the treatment room that all is well. I'd often thumb nailed this larger event as the Big Bloom, which is a milder phrase than the Big Bang, and with its appearance the creation of worlds unfold.

"Do something," I said to the ocean.

It came up again to meet me. I went to my knees and touched.

Silence.

Then I realized, I'd have to put sunscreen on my nose if I didn't want to catch a burn from the sun through the windows in the morning. I walked backwards from the beach looking as long as I could, turned, and went all the way back up the stairs and back up the other stairs and the yet other smaller stairs to my bedroom and into the walk-in closet that Dad and I built when I was in high school and squeezed some spf 15 out of the white tube. I almost tripped on one of Dad's black dress shoes when I put the sunscreen on my dresser top and turned to walk back into the oddly angled Hemingway style room. I fell into bed, no matter the covers, and as the greater dawn broke over the triangle shaped walls, my eyelids grew heavy with the sound of Dad's snores, again louder than the TV and in a competition with the sound of the early morning waves. My head turned ever so slightly on my pillow with a sense that the Old Man was still here, watching over me. I heard the words, "I'm right here."

III

Sensitive Weather

FORTY SOMETHING?

"Isn't it amazing that we're here on this planet? And alive? That we have fingers and toes and eyes? I think I'm starting to appreciate just being alive."

"I never think about that. You're going on and on about that, and I'm thinking about the sawdust on the floor that your brother-in-law left yesterday. And that we need to vacuum it up."

I could hardly hear him through the sound of the giant Hoover in my hands, but I got the drift of what he meant. Maybe I was too into feeling I was special or tuned in or better than others, on the other hand, Dad just is. I wondered if I should feel a tinge of guilt?

"Over there. You missed a spot."

"It might scratch the paint."

No response.

Dad was seated in one of the captain's chairs in the doorway of the dining room wearing his short, white terrycloth bathrobe and light blue boxer shorts. The captain's chairs have arms that extend out so you can rest your elbows on them. The arms on the mate's chairs only come out so far so your elbows slip. Mom would sit on the mate's chair at her end of the dining room table. I would sit next to her at her right, the place of honor she'd say, not always on a captain's chair.

"Just being alive!"

He points again. "Vacuum here."

"Why?"

"Dust!"

"Where?" The kitchen floor was wide lines of red and turquoise linoleum that had been laid down in the mid 1950s. It was faded with flecks of white and continued again in the Florida room where it was once upon a time, chiseled into the shapes of large seahorses underneath the overhead fans. Now there was thick carpet there. The earliest nickname my parents gave the house was, *The Sea Ranch,* because the yard was a plot of ground from old Florida with what Dad thought were too many palmetto palms, jasmine, and overgrown sea grape trees. Every weekend, he was outside in his undershorts and T-shirt with a shovel and broom trying to tame his acre of overgrown property. I'd seen this floor swept and mopped a thousand times but never had I seen anyone vacuum it. There were wood shavings on it from some carpentry work my brother-in-law had done on a leak under the kitchen ceiling and fresh new paint laid down on the floor molding. My brother-in-law said there were some leaks in this house that couldn't be taken care of, next hurricane, it would leak all over again. I flipped the brown cord over the vacuum cleaner. I felt mischievous. "I might scratch the linoleum."

"You against the Union?"

I knew this was a joke but I couldn't figure it out. "The Union?"

He let it go.

"Don't you ever think what will happen after you go? I mean, you buy land. It's the Earth, you know?"

"Don't say, you know."

"I know. But your own generation keeps buying up things, and polluting the land. What about your grandchildren, and their children?

"I never think about it."

"What *do* you think, Dad?"

"It will all blow up anyway after I'm gone."

"You rich guys always say that! No, it won't."

He gave me a look.

"I mean, what if...what if it doesn't...all blow up? Then what?"

The phone rang on the kitchen table. He pointed to the phone. I got it. It was a counselor from North Carolina who had seen my brochure and wanted to refer a client of hers to come to Florida to work. I was in my red swimsuit with white racing stripe, no shirt, and didn't feel dressed for this call.

"What about CraniOcean?"

"CraniOcean?" CraniOcean was on the brochure. For a moment, I'd forgotten what I'd called it. I turned off the vacuum cleaner. Her client loved the ocean, swam regularly, and the counselor felt it would be a good match. How did the counselor ever find my brochure? Someone had given it to her in New York City.

"Is there any conflict with psychological counseling?" she asked.

"No, none at all. It's deep work and a lot gets done. Afterwards, give it a break and then she can start processing again, with you."

"Perfect."

"She may even have a better sense of why she's going for counseling in the first place."

She laughed.

"What does your client do for a living, by the way? Can she make the time to come down here?"

"She's an osteopath."

Dad motioned to hang up the phone and get back to work.

"Tell me more about CraniOcean."

"Well," I said, "if you can follow all of this. Each practitioner has his or her own approach. CraniOcean is a synthesis of different approaches that I've learned along the way, and sometimes "unlearned." It's intuitive bodywork and massage therapy in a blend with something called, Craniosacral Therapy. It's done on a massage table, or in the ocean. It's calming and restful, but it works."

"Wonderful, I'll tell my client!"

Dad gave me a look.

I ended the call. "Uh, Dad? Someone's going to be flying in next week to treat with me at the house."

"At the house?"

"Well, it will be between the beach and the house."

"A girl?"

"An osteopath, Dad."

His head dropped and he pulled it back. "With you?"

"Is that okay?"

He looked at the floor. "How old are you?"

"Forty-six?"

His head pulled back. "I thought you were in your thirties, forties."

"Forty-something?"

A couple of my sisters had asked me to stay at the house and look over Dad as his rescuer. This would mean extending my return to L.A., but now this would work out great. I had some clients in the Palm Beaches, but off and on, not like the type that usually flies to my location in L.A. for a long weekend to treat. Also, this would be the first time I'd get to use the house, the pool, and the ocean. It would be an experiment!

"I'm off to Homecoming next weekend, with the girls."

"Homecoming?"

"For my award."

Dad had quite a collection of them from the Alumnae Association, including the distinguished, "Last Drop Award," which is a colorful but huge print of a cowboy on the range kneeling down in front of his horse and holding out his upturned Stetson Hat which contains a last few drops of water. 'He gave it all,' Dad would say of the print. Dad had never missed a homecoming at Stetson since his graduation which was more than fifty years ago, but I'd only been to two or three in my life. We would all drive up in his Cadillac to the town of Deland for the weekend which is about two hundred miles into the center of the state. It pained me that I might miss his award ceremony, but then the house would be empty and less stress on the client, I'd hoped. "Oh. Well, is it okay?"

"You're not coming to Homecoming?"

Award ceremony or Homecoming, what did it matter? I'd graduated from the same University as Dad, and going up there for the weekend was more or less a family tradition. "No."

It was settled.

He became thoughtful. "What about your girl?"

"Susan? Yells too much, I don't know."

"Won't hurt you."

"I broke up with Susan, okay? Dad, it's not a girlfriend, it's a job!"

"A job? With you?"

I couldn't believe it either.

SWIMMING WITH DOLPHINS

Dad and I got dressed and went over the bridge to Dunkin' Doughnuts in West Palm and picked up some things at Home Depot. When we came back, I unloaded the car, put the things in the garage and headed upstairs to review some notes. He'd gone into his room to take a nap. It all felt too soon and I didn't know if I could pull this off. I'd done work in the ocean out in front of the house before and in the pool but only with family and friends. It can sometimes be a little daunting when an osteopath comes in to call, and this one was flying in from New York City. I'd been invited to New York City for a few months in the early part of the year but it wasn't for a play of mine on Broadway, it was to do bodywork and mostly on artists and professionals there. What could I possibly do for an osteopath that her own colleagues couldn't, I kept asking myself. An osteopath is a "doctor" right? I could hardly pronounce the woman's name.

I sat next to the window and opened my soft leather journal. I looked out at the bright ocean. Freeport was only ninety miles away from my bedroom as the crow flies. I remembered an old Bahamian woman last time I was there who said, "We share the same weather. We share the same storms." I was in one of the puddle-jumper-planes typical to the Bahamas and behind me was an old woman with day-glow eye shadow. She was visiting her great grandchildren on the tiny island of Bimini. A dark storm raged in the distance and there was lightning striking over the ocean. The storm was headed due east. There were only a few of us in the plane and to calm myself, I shouted to the old woman that the storm might go all the way to Florida! I'd never realized how close Florida and the Bahamas were. I'd been to the Bahamas over the last few years, but it was more to get familiar with dolphins and to play with them in the water and find out what they were about.

It was only recently that I'd been warmly invited back to work with dolphins and people in the water at the same time. I turned to a page in my journal. There was a story there about a large woman from Argentina of light skin with light brown hair, a New Ager, well into middle age. She was the type that was into dolphins and angels as a love and light sort of thing and it about turned my stomach. I don't know why. She'd had new age tattoos inked down the back of each of her arms in preparation for her meeting with the dolphins. There were a lot of stories in my journal, stories I never really knew what to do with, maybe put on the stage someday as plays. There was a note about dolphins as "super facilitators." It started to come back to me.

The first time I swam with dolphins was in a pen in Key West. I guess I was like anyone who wanted to swim with dolphins; I hoped it would change my life forever, amen. The pen was off a brackish intercoastal canal and there were docks leading out to where you would pet the dolphins and even get in the water with them. It was a rainy day and I paid my money and some guy pointed to where I was supposed to go and I got into the water. There were three of them in there and at first, I was a little scared. They were bigger than me. I got a little more comfortable and decided to give them time to come over and play with me, but no matter what splashing or pleas I made, they wouldn't come near me. I was miserable going into the water and I came out even more miserable. The guy at the gate wouldn't give me my money back and I got into an argument with him. He shooed me off the property and I just had time to pull my Levi's over my old baggies. I got in Dad's Cadillac and headed north back to Palm Beach on I-95 and I was crying big tears about how awful life was and how unfair and nobody could get a break, not even nice guys from nice dolphins, and about when I passed Ft. Lauderdale, it hit me, I was feeling so miserable that I would have avoided me too. I didn't even want to be in my own company, but there was no where else in the car I could go. I wanted to crawl out of my skin and there was nothing for me to do but face it.

Maybe that was a lesson too.

What I mean by *super facilitators* is that dolphins, like the very best body workers and massage therapists, meet you where you are. They have no judgment on who or what you ought to be. They meet you where you are without regard to nationality, religion, race, age, creed, smell. This is a lesson in itself. Each dolphin responds precisely to where you are, moment by precious moment, in thought and in feeling. And because they have no "hidden agenda" going on, other than to survive and to play and to explore when you are with them, they are different with each person and express a mighty kindness. What's interesting is that however personal they may be, there is always an invisible boundary and an essential dignity and integrity to their interaction. In other words, they are deeply intimate with each person and yet impersonal.

Upledger once told us all a story in the Bahamas. It was kind of a campfire story at the end of a long day of treatment sessions. It was about how he got interested in working with dolphins and craniosacral therapy. He was vacationing on the West Coast of Florida with a doctor friend of his who for some reason became determined to prove that dolphin and human communication was a fraud. Upledger didn't know what his friend had against dolphins but let it go. Later, his friend jumped into the ocean and started to thrash around, as if he was drowning. There are a lot of dolphins on the Gulf shores but not one showed up to save him. And so his friend had proved the point: it was phony.

The next morning. Dr. Upledger, or "Dr. John" as he is known affectionately, went looking for his friend but couldn't find him. He went out to the beach. Then he saw something in the distance but couldn't make out what it was. Two dolphins were at either side of his friend's arms, supporting him. The dolphins swam with his friend like this all the way into the shore, into about three feet of water, and slipped away to go back to sea. His friend was hardly conscious, and Dr John grabbed him out of the water. Dr. John soon learned that very early that morning, his friend had swam out as far as he could, however, he had gone so far that he had become virtually exhausted. He didn't plan on this. He could no longer tread water and began to sink, at which moment, two dolphins came up from below—out of nowhere—and hooked their dorsal fins under each of his arms, securing him for the journey back to shore.

I breathed in the hot sunlight coming in through the open bedroom windows. I was getting excited about going to the beach and calling out to the dolphins, whatever that would look like. I shaded my eyes and strained to see if there were any dolphins on the water now. I'd only see them out there when I didn't expect to see them. If I tried to see them, I just wouldn't. I'd have to catch them in the corner of my eye.

What was great about the dolphin sanctuary in the Bahamas was that I could always count on them to be there. It wasn't at all like the place in Key West, way back when, and all that was before I'd met the old man. The dolphins at the sanctuary were in a natural lagoon enclosure and had easy access to the ocean by a tributary that led out a small inlet to the beach. Hibiscus flowers, sea grape trees, and colorful gingerbread homes of coral pink and blue looked over the inlet and some days, the water was crystal clear in the lagoon since it was constantly fed by the sea. The dolphins could jump out of the enclosure on nightly swims but most all always came back to the sanctuary. A lot of them had been born there.

I wondered about the controversy about dolphin enclosures versus dolphins in the wild. I did know that dolphins in the wild were very different than the dolphins in the sanctuary, also, to be very cautious when approaching dolphins in the wild. When on guided swims with the sanctuary dolphins in the ocean, wild dolphins rarely show up to check out the play and the action, but when they do, the sanctuary dolphins will snub them. Now, that's attitude! Dolphins in the wild often tend to keep a respectful distance from humans. Many of my classmates who visited the enclosed lagoon in the Bahamas had swum with the dolphins in the wild but longed to get closer to them, touch them, be touched. This is next to impossible in the wild. After all, how would you like it if someone suddenly jumped through the roof of your home and demanded that you make friends?

I'd heard so many stories over the years that it seemed anyone could always go to the Big Island of Hawaii, or even Oahu, and find areas where the wild dolphins school and play with them. But it's a very different form of play than in an enclosure. You can swim out a half mile or so and then find yourself surrounded by hundreds of dolphins. Some of these schools also contain schools of Humpback Whales and Manta Rays. I'd never done a dolphin swim in Hawaii, but from the stories of clients and colleagues, at least one dolphin will usually monitor the swimmer the whole time the swimmer is around the large schools and at a distance of about five feet. No one tells the dolphins to do this but it makes sense, doesn't it? An enthusiastic swimmer with scuba fins out that far from land could be injured inadvertently by the sheer size and variety of the schools. Nevertheless, it's useful to remember that these dolphins are in fact, also wild mammals, and to exercise caution. When in the sanctuary or in the wild, I like to remember that I am on a visit to another's home, and I like to be, what to me, is a good guest.

VERY SENSITIVE CHAOS

Weather? What a strange note: Hurricane Andrew devastated Miami one year after the Gulf War.

I turned another page.

We were in the Upledger Institute research vessel, the *Dolphin Star,* off Freeport, Grand Bahama Island on a blustery day and spotted two wild dolphins at play near a small sand key. The hired captained turned off the engines and Kat Cramblet, as first mate, volunteered to adjust the wench at the bow. The wench suddenly slipped from her hand and sliced through her thumb, almost to the bone. She fell into shock, holding her hand, and moved quietly to the back of the boat. We all gathered, letting the rare opportunity of swimming with the wild dolphins go. Kat had light brown eyes that smiled under a tussle of brown hair and always had a kind word and we collectively began to send or direct energy into her hand, thumb, arm. We were concerned. There were about ten of us, all in training, and we were using a direction of energy technique or "V" spread. This was developed by Dr. Sutherland and thankfully, adopted by Upledger in his training. It not only works to calm skin breaks, but it can also work with neuromuscular tension, headaches, and can even calm the shock from fractures. It sounds unbelievable because it's so simple to do and anyone, really, can learn to do it well. It's a simple matter of making the shape of a "V" with the index and middle finger of one hand, and then making a pistol barrel with the index finger and thumb of the other hand. Then, only energy is directed like a laser from the barrel into the dip of the "V". There is no need to do visualizations or affirmations or prayers, but some do, and this is fine too. Some of us were doing the "V" spread by the book, others were simply doing laying on of hands.

The Captain was on the top deck and had only wanted us to stop for a little while because there were rain clouds threatening two and a half miles out at sea and we'd need time to get the vessel back to its small but safe harbor. But we weren't going anywhere. All of us were focused and intent on sending healing warmth and energy and love into our friend's thumb. It wasn't as if she was a professional "first mate," she was a craniosacral therapist too and she had just been helping out with the wench. The Captain was from the Bahamas and had weathered many storms, he knew the area and its dangers and there was nothing he could do but monitor the storm. Within minutes, his radar showed the clouds coming in closer and closer. Then, incredibly, the clouds began to form a discrete circle around the boat itself. He had never seen this kind of storm activity before. The clouds were in place around the research vessel within twenty minutes. He called our team leader to the top deck, who happened to be Dr. Chas Perry, and exclaimed he was going to quit this job because this was too weird! I and others went up to look at the radar screen. A perfect radius of storm clouds had formed around the vessel now and the dark clouds did not let fall their heavy rain.

Kat began to feel better, although she was still frightened, and Chas was determined to get her off the research vessel and into a hospital. The Captain fired up the engines and we headed back toward our dock, almost four miles away. An ambulance was radioed and the plan was to drop Kat off at an inlet that was closer than our dock. What really shook the Captain was that the cloud pattern maintained its circular integrity above the vessel for the one mile to Kat's drop off point. We all saw what the clouds were doing, but it wasn't important, we were concentrated on sending this young, distraught woman energy and healing warmth. These people were not mystics or shamans. It was just a ragtag collection of massage therapists, physical therapists, occupational therapists, a psychiatrist, an osteopath, but all focused and concentrated in combination with love. At the inlet, we pulled back our hands, Kat said she'd had enough, and the cloud pattern broke up as if on cue.

It was an experience of a kind of theater, a theater too vast to fathom or write about.

Nobody thought much of it. Not everyone saw the radar screen or really noticed the clouds. Meanwhile, we were just grateful that Kat did not lose her finger. "Oh yeah," said, Chas, when I brought it up to him the next day, "Those clouds."

Someone had to record it on the page. The Captain was still weirded out and had gone on a bender. No one wanted to talk about it and no one dared include it in our notes to the Institute. So I sat by myself in the Galley one night and made an entry in the research vessel's log. I added rudimentary drawings of the boat and the clouds to try and show what had happened to us. It was outlandish, almost other worldly. I asked myself if this was a one time event, or an event that could happen again? This was a moment where I began to depart the status quo and look at the big picture. There was something more that wasn't being fully acknowledged or embraced, and perhaps, not just by our team.

It was a missing piece.

I made a note to check the weather when working with the osteopath. But I wasn't sure why she was coming here and I still wasn't sure what I could offer her that her colleagues couldn't. I saw a passage I'd scribbled out as a poem from a book called, *Sensitive Chaos,* by Theodor Schwenk. Strange title, I thought. A buddy of mine from prep school in New England, now a progressive farmer, had told me to read it when I told him on the phone about the circle of clouds.

> Everywhere in nature the elements of air and water mingle in manifold interplay. Every system of rivers, every lake, every sea, is an organic totality with its own circulation, and to each of these belong the air space above it.

I didn't get it. It was kind of like reading a passage from the *Lord of the Rings,* Gandalf to Frodo. Where was my head at when I wrote this down? Organic totality, I said aloud. Was there something else going on here that nobody was talking about? I could just touch it but could not articulate it. Maybe this was for the best. Some of nature's mysteries are not easily repeatable as experiments and better left alone. I leaned forward in my green canvas chair and turned my face to look at the sky. Sky. Blue sky. Clouds. I sang softly, Blue sky, smiling at me, nothing but blue sky do I see. Blue birds, all the day long, nothing but blue birds from now on. So what? Why not take a look at this? It couldn't hurt. Clouds are composed mostly of water, just like our bodies are composed mostly of water. Weather flows with charged electricity, just as our bodies flow with charged electricity. Weather is always working to balance itself, hence high and low pressure systems, and our bodies are always working to balance themselves, hence high and low.... No way! I repressed these thoughts immediately. I sat back into my chair and placed the cool bottoms of my feet up on the warmed wood windowsill. I was a detective on a case now and went back to the story I'd scribbled down about the nice Argentinean woman.

TRINIDAD AND TOBAGO

I thumbed through some pages on dolphins and their miraculous power to heal.

Where was that Argentinean woman now? She had been so terribly frightened of the water, if not of herself.

My journal says that today Lordes wanted to wear a diving mask and snorkel and I disapproved. I couldn't say this openly. The group had been working for two days now but this was the first day I'd worked with Lordes. On the first day, Lordes, not her real name, had complained to the group that she didn't feel connected within herself and that this was unusual for her. She said, maybe she'd never really felt connected in her body. She would move her palms over the center of her body to try and describe this. She had a sense of connection once upon a time but didn't know where it went. She didn't feel very good about herself, and I myself appreciated her honesty in saying that. She was on the edge of tears. She said she hoped that with the dolphins, she could somehow reconnect to herself and with others. I looked at the new age tattoos on the back of her arms showing from behind her T-Shirt and knew I would have to put my personality preferences aside. I had served a lot of people like her at the Bodhi Tree and had about had my fill but knew on some level precisely what she was talking about. I hadn't had a chance to work with her, and didn't know if I would. Maybe we didn't have the proper chemistry with each other.

We were arranged in groups on a concrete shelf in the water

about four feet deep and each person had two or three therapists working with them. There were four small groups, almost like our own little pods. Every now and then, a person being floated, freed from the pressures of gravity, would roll and break away to visit with the other groups in the pod, then spontaneously settle in a new location. After several years of learning to treat each other as therapists in the waters of the Bahamas, and of playing with the dolphins, just like the tourists would, we would be working with dolphins and with bonafide patients too! And now, out of almost half a million craniosacral therapists, through the Institute alone, practicing worldwide, in offices, clinics, spas, hospitals, we few felt vastly privileged to be part of the first team out to explore the possibilities!

There was an observation deck built of wood with a palm thatched roof and the few therapists who weren't in the water that particular day were taking notes, since one of our first challenges was to develop the medical notations for work with dolphins, for example, what is an appropriate description for when a dolphin makes contact with the instep of a foot? Is that a contact, a touch, a hit? The concrete shelf was part of a pool used for tourists coming in on a flat bottomed boat from Port Lucaya. The tourists would be led up the long ramp from the boat and some would be allowed to dangle their feet and pet the dolphins with a trainer standing by, while others would take photographs from the observation deck, which was now cordoned off from tourists.

Lordes was the very last one to come down the mossy wooden slats on the side of the pool, complete with her snorkel gear, and I glanced over at my assistant for the morning, Ada. Ada was from Puerto Rico and had blue eyes like the meeting of sky and ocean with dark and silver hair that flashed in the light like undersea. I liked her, everybody did. She was like, Dolphin Girl, and could swim like a dolphin without even trying to. She gave a hint of a smile and a shrug as Lordes's large body landed, sending ripples throughout the stillness of the work already in progress. She went face down in the water with her mask and snorkel and I could tell Ada was as unsure as I was where to place hands. We held the space, one might say, without physically touching for a few moments, then, Lordes rolled and went to her knees and broke through the tangle of her light brown hair with her fingers to tear the mask off. "No," she said. "This is not right."

Ada went over and placed a hand on her shoulder and I felt grateful for that. Lordes handed the mask to me and I quietly removed it to the floating platform that surrounded us on four sides. She slowly fell back into the water into Ada's open hands. She evidentially felt supported by Ada's gentle touch under her broad shoulders and calmed.

I dropped down to her feet to scan, or arc, the energy field surrounding her body. Time seemed to slow down almost to a stop and expand. My hands got what she had said about not feeling connected almost instantly. There was little discernible core in this woman's body, it was broken lines going up from around her tailbone, or sacrum, to her head, or cranium, and it was a false core, not true. And there were snakes coiled all around, dark snakes, up the legs, in the thighs, and particularly concentrated at her left shoulder area. I wondered if the dolphins had any familiarity with snakes, at least sea snakes and half asked them. Then I remembered a comment that Ada had made the day before about asking the dolphins to do what they needed to do, rather than our telling them what we thought they needed to do or ought to do. This made the clearest sense. I brought it back to asking the body of this large woman in front of me, silently, "Could you show me what you need done?"

I had no idea where to begin or what could be done for her at all. This was a woman who had spent a great deal of time in the United States, an advanced practitioner of several different styles of bodywork and a self confessed "therapy junkie" who had over years encountered a range of sophisticated spiritual modalities. She'd worn a T-shirt at breakfast that morning which read, "Part Time Angel." She was having her tea and toast at a table which was underneath a print of a tiny cherubim looking askance, from the Sanzio portrait, La Madonna di Sisto. As a joke, I pointed to the T-Shirt and to the print and asked, "What's your other part time job?"

She answered with a smile, "Part time devil."

"Well, I guess we all are part time angels and part time devils!" She laughed.

Now, with all these snakes wrapped deep inside her body, I backed off and dropped into a place of not knowing. I didn't know what was to happen next, if anything. Over the past two days, the dolphins had come in close to each patient we were working with, and rather quickly. If they didn't brush up against the patient or touch the patient or make contact, almost as if with intention, they would sweep by and swish their fins and tails to send up a pulsation of water against the person's body. Now, they kept their distance. They would not approach this woman even as they were approaching the others.

On the first day, they spent time at the bottoms of each patient's feet and it was the only area of the body they would contact. On the second day, they avoided the feet almost entirely and made contact with the patients' heads. It was peculiarly similar to the way a craniosacral therapist would work. First, very respectfully at the feet, and then later at the head, but only with permission. The dolphins were not trained for this behavior and were learning on the job. This was the first day the dolphins would begin, of their own behest, to make contact with the whole body of each patient that was being floated. They were learning, day by day, just as we were learning because this was new to us too. I said silently to this large woman's body in front of me, "Show me what you need," but now I also directed this request to include the two dolphins we were working with, Tobago and Trinidad, so that it would be as one body. "Show us." The dolphins continued to keep their distance.

The sun was hot on the still water and I looked out at the other therapists floating their patients, each group being careful to keep the patients' noses above water. There was a salty breeze, and a gull landed on the platform behind me and began its calls. After some minutes of this it seemed the calls of the seagull were somehow working in concert with the clicks and whistles of the dolphins. I let my imagination drift with the sounds and the exceedingly rare harmonies of their dissonances. Squawk, squawk, squawk! Click, click! Hadn't the ocean been fine tuned over millions of years, not just hundreds of years, with its inhabitants all working together as predators, parasites, prey, all as an interdependent whole? There are times in the silence of working with dolphins when wisdom arises.

Now I wondered, was there really such a thing as independence? We humans were a recent arrival on the planet and perhaps had not yet perceived the delicate balance of the sea creatures in their great water homes. I wondered if anything in the sea was truly independent of anything else in the sea. Even above the sea...! Independence does not occur in nature, if we bother to look, only in our own overworked and addled brains. It doesn't occur in the human body. How could we as a species have become so tragically wrong, so deluded? What organ in the human body is independent of any other organ? What could the heart do without the liver, the liver without the blood, the blood without the body? If any one of our organs declared its independence from the others, we would have a major disorder.

I thought of an archeological finding in Pakistan in the summer of 2001 and how whale fossils from 50 million years ago were discovered and the whales had legs! I thought of other stories, myths, theories, of whales and dolphins as once having been land mammals and then going back to the sea. They went from the sea to the land and back again! Click, click! Squawk, squawk, squawk! Who was I to say there couldn't be a kind of connection between the dolphins and the seagulls? Or with us, for that matter?

The dolphin trainer, Megan, would intermittently feed the dolphins mackerel, and the dolphins would be still, and then go back to work with us. Megan had a thin black whistle in her mouth but never used it, as was her custom with the tourists, and we all very much appreciated this small favor of hers. Now and then, Megan would clap her hands silently and smile to show her approval to each of the dolphins for their treatment of a patient. Megan had long, rusty blonde hair with a corporate T-Shirt and Bermuda shorts. We all felt she had a sense of what these two dolphins could do, although we dared not compel her to talk openly about it. The Trainers who worked there had a deep and abiding respect for each and every one of the dolphins who lived here, were knowledgeable about the ways of the sea, and most professional. The seagull suddenly leaped from the platform and sped just over Lordes's body and beyond the enclosure. I noticed this flight, as if on the proper cue, my hand slowly followed the seagull's flight path and went down under the water and turned to come up to rest on Lordes's sacrum, or tailbone. There seemed to be some energy moving inside there but Ada's hand had just arrived at about the same spot. I smiled to myself and let my hand back off a little. I'd been put on this job by Dr. Perry, the head of our team, to play the role of lead therapist, and Ada had been able to anticipate my every move. I myself could not anticipate what my next move would be. Again, Ada and I had caught on that there was to be no "lead" therapist here but the dolphins.

Within moments of our contact, Lordes's body rolled over in place in the water and stopped. There was fear. She may have gone too far, but I wouldn't put a judgment on it. Her body shook and she rolled backwards to Ada and I for air. She was now in a sheer panic to catch her breath.

"Safety," I silently mouthed to Ada.

Ada nodded.

We shifted on our knees to accommodate and we both held Lordes in our arms and intentioned nothing but feelings of safety and care and comfort for Lordes. She settled. I nodded to Ada. Ada nodded to me. Somehow, I thought of the Old Man saying: Be like the heart, dependent on all the other organs in the body, but make a contribution to Life. *Be like the heart.* The dolphins came closer. Something had shaken loose. Things had calmed down. Now, Trinidad touched Lordes's ankle and leg. Lordes stretched and spread out her legs and arms on the gentle surfaces of the water. Tobago came near and touched the left side of Lordes's head. Trinidad came around and touched the right side of Lordes's head. They remained at her head with their rostrums, or beaks, making gentle contact. Then they backed off and away. Lordes knew the dolphins were in touch with her. She smiled. I again said, silently, "What is it you need? What, if anything, can we do?" Trinidad, the male dolphin and younger than Tobago, now returned and placed his beak at the very crown of Lordes's head and stayed there. A whisper thin line of harmony shot from Lordes's head all the way down to her sacrum. The line grew in intensity inside her core and Trinidad backed away. It was just enough.

Now, the snakelike forms around her shoulders began to loosen, one by one. Space began to open at her hips. Ada and I were now able to magnetize our hands to these energy forms and slowly pull them out of her body, one by one, sometimes in clusters, and send them away to wherever such things go. The whisper thin line of harmony needed some more support somehow. I wondered if the dolphins might come back and assist,

I may never fully understand what was to follow. Tobago, the older female dolphin, came in and placed her beak on the right side of Lordes's head, then, moved it to Lordes's crown, almost exactly where Trinidad had been before. Tobago gave a flick of the rostrum, just as an Energy Worker would, as if sending bad energy away from the woman's body. Then she placed her rostrum back on the woman's crown.

I thought, "Amazing." For I'd just had the thought, "Are you two working the same way as we are? Are you tracking the progress too?"

Within seconds, I felt a pulsation of water surround my legs and tickle my waist and I felt compelled to turn around. From below the water Trinidad literally waved his fin at me, going up in the water slightly and nodding his head up and down. Tobago was the one in physical contact with the woman, but Trinidad was the one that answered...a mere thought! I took Trinidad's answer as a big YES! In working with dolphins, it seemed that I had to pay as much attention to what was going on within and without — all at same time. I admired their sheer speed to pick up a thought and bounce it like a ball in a spirit of play. Then I doubted. Maybe Trinidad wasn't answering "my" thought but just doing a trick under the water to get fish from Megan? I turned my head around and the trainer wasn't feeding fish, wasn't even near us.

I asked the question again, inwards with greater depth. "Are you with us?" Again Trinidad waved his fin and nodded his head up and down, this time somewhat breaking the surface of the water. I felt delighted and refocused on the growing line of harmony throughout the woman's core. What if they were tracking the line of harmony too! But I still wasn't sure. It could have all been in my imagination. Tobago dropped away from the woman and went deep. Then I felt a slight bang on my head. Tobago had placed the tip of her beak at the side of my head and rested it there, slightly at an angle to the surface of the water and out of my direct line of sight. Tobago, not Trinidad! Within seconds, there was a subtle feeling of energy moving in my body. I thought, "Whoops, protocol!" I hoped no one had noticed. This was awkward. I started to direct this energy to Lordes, for as therapists we had been instructed that anytime one of the dolphins would send a therapist energy, to kindly ask the dolphin to redirect that energy and warmth back to the person we were working with. But unlike the many other times I'd requested this of the dolphins, my instinct was now to be still, do nothing.

I recalled a complaint I'd had when Trinidad nodded his head for the second time, and again it was only a thought. I didn't voice it out loud to Ada. I silently complained to myself that this was such a slow and awkward way of communication between us, this bobbing up and down under the water, and for a moment, I mourned that humans and dolphins could not be in better touch than use of sign language. Then, I began to feel my own core fill from the sacrum up and cranium down and it had the feeling of fluid, cool rising up from within. Cerebrospinal fluid (csf)? It couldn't be. I didn't know that I could feel this too. I gently closed my eyes to receive this. Was a line of harmony faintly turning luminous throughout my own core? I had never felt this sensation in my body. I could sense a bioluminescent quality. Was this the feeling my hands had given to others for so many years? There would often come a time in sessions when a luminous blue line of harmony would arise and fill the person's core. And sometimes there would be several lines of harmony that would balance and align at once. It always occurred in silence, but the feeling in the room would be big.

Was this my answer? Was this what no one was talking about, or wouldn't talk about? Could it be that man and dolphin were each working in concert to align the lines of harmony at the core? Because the core is where everything comes together, the *axis mundi* of the body. Tobago backed off from the side of my head and dropped back into the water without a sound. There was a space of silence. In this space, lines from a poem surfaced through my body and mind: *We suffer the same.*

Suffer? Who is "we"?

I couldn't place the words.

What could it mean? Who is suffering?

Then I realized. It was a line from the thirteenth century mystical poet, Rumi, scribed in his timeless Persian masterpiece, *The Mathnawi,* which literally translates as, *The Ocean.*

This is the poem in full. The person mentioned at the end of the poem, "Shams," is Rumi's dear friend and teacher. It seemed it could be a song to all of us in that moment, a song from the dolphins.

A BOWL

Imagine the time the particle you are
returns where it came from!
The family darling comes home. Wine,
without being contained in cups,
is handed around.
A red glint appears in a granite outcrop,
and suddenly the whole cliff turns to ruby.
At dawn I walked along with a monk
on his way to the monastery.

"We do the same work," I told him. "We suffer the same."
He gave me a bowl.
And I saw:
            the soul has this shape.
Shams,
you that teach us and actual sunlight,
help me now,
being in the middle of being partly in my self,
and partly outside.

Had I gone over the edge? Had I gone off the deep end? I
couldn't know. But there was such a feeling of peace surrounding us all, I knew that even if I had, it couldn't hurt me. Tobago
was already working with someone else in our pod. Trinidad returned to place the bottom tip of his beak at the woman's hair-
line. Her head dipped a little in the water with the weight of
Trinidad's beak, sent a soft ripple like a halo, and another smile
appeared on her face. Clean energy, freed of emotional debris and
stress, was running through her body all the way down to her
knees. Ada nodded to me that a vibration was occurring at the
woman's ankles. I realized Ada was more a feeling person, that is
to say, more kinesthetic, where I was more visual, and that all
along she had been focused on monitoring and sensing the tight
connective tissues as they would loosen around the woman's arms,
legs, hips. What might have looked like "snake forms," was to Ada,
simply tight, neuromuscular contraction and its release. Trinidad
departed to work with others for awhile. I thought, "Wow, her core
is connected and in hook up! What next?" I tried to give a nod
to Ada. Ada, however, was focused on palpating the rapid physical changes in the woman's body and wasn't impressed with what
my insights might have been. I felt alone. It was a feeling of be-

ing alone in the Universe, but the Universe as just another structure somehow out there in...the Universe. What is the source of this feeling, I wondered. I looked at the three others floating in the water and being held gently by their highly sensitized therapists. When a craniosacral therapist and patient work together, they are blended and their Nonconcious minds are merged, as if one. I recalled that at the group discussion that morning, Lordes had said she kept the group in mind when she herself received treatment, *the pod,* and all of us as therapists had observed that her attention wasn't just on her own process, but outside of herself too. For her T-Shirts, tattoos, and junk food therapists, Lordes had a sincere concern for other people. I wondered if my impulse to consider the others now was part of Lordes's process? Had she felt alone in the Universe? Still, the quiet blend of patients, therapists, and dolphins was fascinating to observe.

I saw a dolphin leap high and splash in an enclosure beyond ours, as if it too wanted to participate in the blend. I felt for it, for a moment, and I wondered if the other dolphins in Sanctuary Bay had already been part of the group blend too? It wasn't all that inconceivable; it was likely. Ada's concentration on Lordes brought me back, and I refocused on the work at hand. Lordes's core hadn't fully settled and integrated but was running up from the base of the sacrum like a laser with a fullness of energy and light.

Then Trinidad returned and placed his beak on Lordes's open palm and a slight shudder went through her whole body. With this, Lordes's core began to mend and integrate, ever so slowly. After what seemed a long time, Trinidad slipped away from her palm, then reappeared from under the water at Lordes's other open palm and gently placed his beak there.

I brought to mind a move I'd perform soon after I'd started working on the body, before I'd had formal training. In those days,

I would often place hands gently over each of the person's hands and then over each of the feet, not always in that order, like the old man had done with my mother at the vineyard. Anyhow, what Trinidad was doing sure looked like something the Old Man would do. My logical brain kicked into gear. I wondered, just as we were taking our cues from the dolphins, were they taking their cues from us? If so, could this mean that the dolphins, despite their trained behavior and operant conditioning, would be different in their approach with each new practitioner and each new person? Bear in mind that the dolphins were not prepared for this beforehand. No one had given them any special instructions on how to be with us. Each of us was as different as each of them.

I gave it to the mystery.

Trinidad had remained at Lordes's palm and slipped away, but what Ada and I felt was love. It's too easy to forget as intuitive body workers and massage therapists, with all of our techniques and credentials, that love does it all. The feeling resonated within and beyond this woman's body to merge with the feeling of the water itself, which was connected by the small tributary to the ocean. "Love," I silently mouthed to Ada.

"Love," she nodded and smiled.

Lordes's light brown eyes were closed against the salt water and sun, but she received this. She had a blissful smile. Then, her whole body slowly turned, she went under the water and without a feeling of panic, just a nice, easy roll. She came up again and breathed easily. This surprised us. Then, she rolled again, but just as her body rolled, Trinidad again appeared. Lordes, eyes closed, somehow needed her neck and face to remain up out of the water, so we supported her at her stomach. Then, Trinidad touched her lips with his lips. They remained in a kiss for several minutes. Ada and I nodded. It was love. When Trinidad slipped away, Lordes rolled onto her back. Then Tobago, the female, came up and touched her under her right arm, that is, she moved Lordes's arm away and touched just under the side of Lordes' right breast with her beak. With this, there was what could only be described as an opening of this woman's heart, gentle at first, then deepening and spreading throughout her body in a fullness of feeling. I couldn't exactly understand this at first, because Tobago's beak was not directly on Lordes's physical heart. But the line of harmony now calibrated into its fullness, blossoming like a blue star flower just above her forehead. The little blue flower danced on the invisible wellspring of energy there. The water glistened around her long hair and her smile merged with the sunlight.

The session was over. Ada, in her role as Dolphin Girl, slipped away under the water, brought her palms to her sides and gave herself a gentle push toward the dolphins. Her whole body flowed in the stillness.

ANOTHER PRETTY DOLPHIN STORY?

I stood in the water back by the steps and looked back, filled with admiration for the dolphins and their perception. On some level, I had always assumed that only people could be wise.

I thought, "Wow, this is so cool. I've got to write it in my journal and put it in a book or a play." And then I asked, inwardly, if I could write about this session. Both Tobago and Trinidad jumped out of the water from different sides of the enclosure and both shook their heads "no." It didn't seem that they were performing a trick. I asked again. Again they jumped, again they said "no." That's what I saw, not what I felt. I could not understand why they'd say "no" to me. I determined never to write about this event, or anything about the dolphins, out of respect to them. After all, I did ask. On the other hand, there have been those few times when I did something, even though I heard intuitively not to do it, just to see what would happen; it's a piece of mischief I haven't yet gotten rid of, and there have sometimes been rough consequences.

I got out of the water feeling piqued and went to the observation deck for my towel, and for the first time, noticed that almost every single one of the women therapists were changing into clothes shaded of blue and white, and it stayed with me. It was a small thing, but these colors would be worn by the therapists casually, outside of the work situation too. Nobody had been talking about it openly, or could. And I couldn't talk about it openly myself, couldn't put it into words. I recalled how I suspected that on some level, these women therapists had already been working with shimmering blue lines in their own practices and felt a tinge of joy! There was an infinite array of lines and the patterns of lines, enough to go around for everyone, whatever "lines" anyone wanted to see within the context of their discipline or training.

I looked away from my journal. Why did I write a note about this? Colors were merely the surfaces of things, not the source.

(Wisdom is knowing the source of things.)

I looked at the gambling boat out over the horizon, my name for the thing. It was a small pleasure cruise ship and would take passengers out from the Palm Beach Inlet, every day and every night, to gamble in the international waters. It was all lit up and heading south and it could keep heading south to Miami and never come back for all I cared. I didn't like the monotony of the thing. It cluttered the ocean, an ocean that had never asked to be cluttered. Was I adding to the clutter of ideas? Then I remembered something Upledger had said early on about his work with sparkling blue lines he called, vectors, which were more or less stick figures that he would see in a body, just from the corner of his eye, and work to put into place. What had I been so disturbed about? My seeing these other lines wasn't important, after all, it couldn't be, for I wasn't important, and my thumbnail references for these other lines rather tawdry and vague.

I was in conflict.

The last night some of us were at a bar in Port Lucaya and dancing and rum was flowing and I told Lordes that I had a theater background and felt a need to write about the session with the dolphins and asked her permission if I could and she was all for it and excited about getting the word out there and telling her friends and even getting students to do this too and it all sounded kind of wonderful but then I had a flash of a feeling of raw ambition and began to feel ugly and dirty inside. And I thought, "Had the session mattered at all?" It was as if the session benefit for her was lost in a moment to feelings of personal pride. I looked back at the gambling ship with its lights on, taking up the view. The hard work would amount to just another pretty dolphin story to add to the clutter of humanity so that good hearted men and women could be led astray in their evolution by more ideas, more impossible ideals, more shit.

"Watch."

What happened after we got out of the water? I turned back to the page in my journal, ah yes! Later that morning, after we'd taken our showers on the docks and headed toward our vehicles, Lordes quietly confided to Ada that just under her right breast resides what she calls her "secret heart." This was known to neither Ada nor I before or during the session, but Tobago knew. How could a woman have a secret heart under her right breast? A heart that was not her physical heart? Lordes had been a sometime follower of Tibetan Buddhism, along with all her other new age and spiritual paths, and this secret news was shared with her many years before by a Tibetan Lama she knew and trusted. Her Lama told her that she had her heart and also her secret heart.

Tobago knew.

Ada and I were astonished.

And then there was a cockroach on the ceiling? I couldn't figure out this note in my journal. Then it dawned on me. Ada and I continued to work with Lordes during the second and last session of the day, the afternoon session, before it all would vanish into infinity like a work of Theater Art. During this session, a cockroach appeared on the ceiling above our treatment table. I paid it little attention as such things are common in the Islands. But it soon became essential to do some rather deep work inside of Lordes's mouth. Then something most extraordinary hap-

pened that this Facilitator has never seen or witnessed before or
since. As we worked, a flurry of cockroaches and spiders released
out of Lordes's mouth and from under her tongue, faery-like,
making space for yet a deeper opening for her. Again, Ada simply monitored the changes in the tissue with her hands, and as
neither of them said anything aloud about these images, I let it
go, reminding myself that knowing "why" is most often a luxu-
ry and it wasn't important anyway. Just another session. My sense
was this woman was now out of danger, what I mean by that is
a danger to the soul, although I won't pretend, like so many others in these interesting times, to know what the soul is. It was
just an intuition I had. She graciously thanked the various levels
of consciousness that she'd touched in the two sessions that day,
and Ada and I thanked her for the great privilege of letting us
work with her. I left the session room early to go for a swim in
the hotel pool, and Lordes sat up on the table and confided to
Ada and others that her mouth felt free and her throat open and
clear and that she felt fully connected in her whole body as if
for the first time in her life! All were most grateful to hear this.
Then she said that for the past several years she'd had the most
curious and painful problem, that whenever she visited someone's
home as a guest, indigenous insects, cockroaches, and large spiders would suddenly appear throughout the house, and this was
an embarrassment and annoyance to her and to her friends. Ada
wasn't sure why Lordes had shared this story with them. When
I heard about it the next day, I thought of Trinidad and the kiss.
Who wouldn't have thought of it? We were all there, we all saw
it, it was the longest kiss.

Trinidad knew.

I had no idea of what had been hidden in the woman's mouth.

LEARNING HOW TO LEARN

I held the soft leather covers of my journal between my hands. What else could I learn from Lordes's sessions, if anything? I often wonder this after sessions, if only to understand that I myself don't even know how to learn. I'm always back to being a beginner and back to learning only how to learn. I just didn't know. I smiled and thought of the dolphins, that kind of half smile they have. I could tell I was still processing Lordes's session for myself. I had some emotional charge going on about this woman, she'd triggered me that night in the bar, and on some level, I was as capable of telling all my friends about the "healing" of the dolphins or writing this story down in a book but really to make a name for myself as maybe even she was, or anyone else for that matter, but it wasn't my purpose. If I set about to do good for the world but really want to have the attention and approval of the world, then that gain in attention and approval is my real purpose. If I set up a healing clinic and deep down really want to be seen by everyone as popular or important, what quality of care and comfort would those coming into the clinic receive? What of the feeling and the deeper resonances of each session?

What was my real purpose?

The dolphins were under no obligation to me personally. They were different with each person. I marveled at how they could be so impersonal yet so intimate. They could even treat others with sounds and from a distance, a full spectra of extraordinary and unique sounds, halos of sounds, far beyond the clicks and whistles that we associate them with. I remembered how I'd thought of the harsh criticisms that angry women had dealt out to me, mean criticisms that could hurt, and at one point when I had let my head lay in the water and float with the dolphins, just for a few brief moments, an insight rose up through my body that these criticisms were only sounds.

They're only sounds.

It was a gift from the dolphins.

How had this woman triggered me? She was only trying to be supportive of my request. She'd even given me her permission to write about her session that day in a book. She was nice about it.

Sounds.

There was one thing for sure, if something triggers me emotionally about another person, that's really something about myself that's being triggered, otherwise, I wouldn't care, would I? I'd make a joke or laugh it off. I wouldn't be all torn up about it inside. The ugly feelings were in me. If I had criticism or remarks about another, even about my sisters, that criticism is somewhere inside and for me to look at. Could it be my sisters? "Nothing personal," they'd said, when a few of them got together one afternoon in the Florida room and circled me like cats and told me never to write about my life or about Dad or the family. These few sisters were in a wildly crazy mood that would pass as quickly as it came, "Don't write!" "You can't write!" At the time, a strong, dry wind lifted off the surface of the ocean and blew over the house, and no one noticed. I wanted to mention it, say something to make them stop. If was as if the sea and sky were getting involved and graciously absorbing the conflict. "Whatever you will ever write in your life will only hurt us!" Ssssss. It was absurd and I wanted to laugh but they would shut me up with loud yowls. Yowwwwl! Another strong, dry wind lifted off the ocean but still no one noticed. These few mature women looked like cats with big ears and noses and claws that needed to be clipped and I was the family dog! I was caught in a catfight and could only bark back! Bark, bark, bark! YOWL! I'm not really sure what started it. Maybe I'd never know. Just one of those things that happen in families sometimes. My sisters are pretty special and wonderful on the whole, and the next day they were their happy selves again. It passed like a storm. It's called the human condition and could happen with anyone. *Judge not lest ye be judged,* still holds true. I knew I could come down on any of them when I was in a bad mood too, I was just as capable of bad manners as they were, or anyone else.

What was this judgment? Had Lordes's comment reminded me of my sisters somehow? We were known in Palm Beach and West Palm Beach as a loving and happy family when we were growing up, and we were, but when Mom died, things changed a little. Things started to fly out of the closet, things none of us could quite understand without Mom's being there to reassure us that we each were special and wonderful. There was so much pain and grief and a dark hole was made in the house by her loss. I felt grateful for the old man's help then and how we repaired the hole together that night to heal it. Even so, it wasn't too long after that I found out something dark had escaped that healing. A house is only as good as the mood of the people in it. Where our house was so filled with love and serenity and safety before, now when my sisters would all come to visit Dad, things hidden would jump and fly out and send us into senseless conflict. Dad would ignore it, go upstairs and take a nap. It takes a kind of quiet strength and wisdom to ignore such things.

Then I remembered the dream I had about Jack Kerouac, something about "demons." Those "demons" were for me to look at and to understand, no one else. We all have them. We just don't have to live by them. They are demons of anger, guilt, fear, blame and are the ruin and terrible grace of the world. They have nothing to do with the vast array of feeling each one of us are capable, feelings of joy, peace, serenity, even of grief. I took in the wet salt air through my nostrils and breathed as I sat in my bedroom chair. The wind was starting to move on the waves, blowing them white and black. I did not think the ocean creatures would sing for me. I thought of the dolphins and their smiles and how three times they seemed to say, "No." "No?" I asked aloud. "Could it have been a joke?" Or did they really mean it?

You can always ask a question of a dolphin but can you accurately interpret the answer when given?

Frankly, I probably wouldn't have written anything down in my journal if the dolphins had nodded, "Yes." Or maybe I would have screwed up the writing of the story. Maybe I would have turned it into some kind of impossible ideal about dolphins and angels as a love and light kind of thing. I was too far into my personal process to laugh, and now, with the feeling of this ugliness and dirt inside, this judgment, what could I possibly offer the Osteopath? What could I offer to anyone? I opened my journal again. There was a note in the edges of the pages: Love does it all.

I couldn't know that Lordes would start to swim with dolphins more than about anybody I knew. Or that she would feel the dolphins had introduced her to whales. She now does deep water dives with Humpback whales off the coast of the Dominican Republic, in between dolphin dives. I couldn't know she would feel more at home in the water than on land and be filled with the cleansing joy of her life!

All I could do was trust.

EMOTIONAL WEATHER PATTERNS

I scribbled a footnote in my journal.

Dad was calling from the stairs. He wanted to invite me out for dinner. He didn't want to be late. I was the only one at the house and had stayed longer with him than I'd planned. I raced into the hallway and the fourth floor bathroom with its odd angled yellow painted walls, brushed my teeth in the bathtub with the thin shower running, scooped off the hard water from my arms and legs before toweling and ran back into my room, still wet. I picked out Dad's light pink sports coat and Club tie, both still in my closet from my last trip home from California. I'd have to wear a tight button shirt around my neck to match, and I put on his black dress shoes with the K-Mart gold buckles. "Virgin, virgin," I sniggered at myself through the rush. "Still in your Dad's shoes?" I stopped for a moment and listened to those words. That wasn't a nice thing for me to say about myself. I ignored it. And I started to sing Mom's song, about what a wonderful world it was if I made it that way, and within minutes found I was up in a good mood! We were going to the Breakers Hotel, just the two of us. This was special.

We turned onto the palm tree lined causeway leading to this legendary Palm Beach hotel and left the Cadillac with the Valet under the wide brushed rococo arches. There was now a wet wind up over the ocean and it blew our coat tails up into our hands. The doorman dressed in black stood aside as we went into the towering brass fitted doors. The great main hall glowed with the light of burnished candelabras in gold and warm pastels and I couldn't help but gawk at the ceiling, like a typical tourist. I'd been coming here since dance cotillion as a kid but the place never ceased to amaze me. I always felt so small here.

It was one of the first grand hotels in South Florida and looked more like a sumptuous palace in Italy or a piece of the Vatican. There were rich tapestries on the walls near the concierge and along the gilded ceilings, too high to make out in detail, frescoes of pastoral scenes of women and children with flowers, grapes, and vases. We turned right along the plush carpet and found our way into the Carousel Room, the same dining room where Dad had gone for his weekly Kiwanis Club meetings for over forty years. The Carousel room was properly considered the new addition to the hotel, having had been built only in the last thirty years, and it was in a circle, like a carousel laid on its side, with tall, heavily draped windows that looked out to the dark ocean.

We were ushered to our small table and carved upholstered chairs were held for us by our waiters as we each sat down. It wasn't what Dad and I were used to and we both tried not to laugh at this courtesy. Coming here was my idea and although I'd hoped to pay for the whole dinner, it now occurred to me I might have to put it on Dad's credit card. Large stately printed menus were placed in front of us and we were soon visited by the mustachioed wine steward, who bowed when Dad brushed him off and motioned him away. I looked around the place. Each table had one waiter for each person and we were no exception. The waiters were dressed in tuxedos with white tails and ties and the light gleamed on the wide serving platters and the upside down brass thing-a-majigs that had been placed on top of the platters. Then the waiters would each place your plate in front of you on a charger and remove a smaller upside down brass thing-a-majig and then step back and disappear noiselessly into the atmosphere. It was a quality of service I could hardly recall, maybe once in San Francisco with Mom and Dad and the family, or a small hotel in the Mira Flores district of Lima after Dad and I had returned from the Amazon and Macchu Picchu. It was our privilege to witness each professional waiter work with each person served rather than demand or rush. It was as it they were angels. It was an image for me of the way the angels serve each one of us with or without our knowing. Dad and I leaned in and admired a simple red rose in an elegant silver vase on our table. I sat back self importantly.

"You know, Dad, there's some people that won't pay me for sessions. I mean, if the sessions go overtime. They won't pay me for the extra time, isn't that weird? They think I'm a healer or something and supposed to give it away for free, as if I live on air or something."

"My time is my stock in trade."

"True, true." I glanced up at the vast chandeliers and the spaces between them. "You know, Dad, this whole dinner is like paying for bodywork and massage."

He grunted. Then took an interest. "Yeah?"

"Hey, I'll be the first one in this room to say bodywork and massage isn't necessary, we can all take care of ourselves, but an evening like this isn't necessary either, I mean, food is food right? We could have eaten in the kitchen from the microwave and survived just as well." I sighed and looked around. There were no words. "But isn't it wonderful to experience this?"

"There you go again. Never look back, always look forward to what's next."

"I'm not looking back, I'm just saying, this is truly wonderful."

He let his eyes drift around the room and said, "Yes, it is."

I called back the wine steward, glasses would be appropriate, not a bottle. Dad agreed and his shoulders relaxed. The rococo ceiling tinted with gold shimmered in the candlelight and glasses of wine. This was rare, Dad and I drinking together. It was totally forbidden by his doctors, along with most his social activities, but now we didn't care. At his age, what did it matter? Dad and I exchanged a look at one point as if this is heaven on earth. After a dinner of surf and turf with a Northern California pinot noir, at over twenty dollars a glass, we found our way down the pink marbled halls to the old Alacazar lounge which fronted the ocean.

"We'll be lucky if we get out of here alive," said Dad.

"We won't stiff them."

He smiled. "They'll skin us alive!"

The lounge looked different from what we both remembered. It used to be called the Alcázar Lounge, and a turquoise light emanated from the wrap around bar. Before, it was a room out of the Arabian Nights with cushions, tapestries, and intimate tables along patina walls, now, all that was gone and the bar was an aquarium covered in Plexiglas with aqua, orange, and yellow pebbles and with a variety of tiny salt water fish and crustaceans. No mistaking this as New Florida. It looked almost radioactive. The bartender, Philippe, set cocktail napkins in front of us. Dad would have his favorite, Dewers on the rocks, but I'd never been a scotch man myself and passed it up for sparkling water with a lemon twist.

There was a Syracuse University basketball game on the television above the bar and we pointed out the colorful fish to each other with our fingers. Some of the fish passed under our open palms. After awhile, Dad pointed and said, "Syracuse." We looked

up at the TV. Dad asked Philippe about the basketball game. It
ended up the bartender had gone to Syracuse University but had
left there because it was too cold, and then he went to Stetson
University in Deland, Florida, but had left there because Deland
was too boring.

I'd gone to Syracuse but turned South and had graduated
from Stetson, like most of the family had, and Dad would soon
be off on his visit to Stetson. "Where'd you dorm at when you
were there?" I asked.

"Nemec Hall."

I glanced at Dad who made no comment but there was a
sparkle in his eye. Philippe came back around to offer us another round, and Dad said, "I'm Nemec."

Philippe couldn't believe it at first. "You're really the Nemec
of Nemec Hall?"

"He is," I said.

Dad looked well dressed too in his soft blue jacket and thick
pink tie, white button shirt, K Mart shoes.

"That's quite a Dad you have there."

I remembered our session. "He's my best friend."

Dad looked away from me and out at the ocean. The powerful lights along the hotel seawall lit up the breakers and the winds
were really kicking up a storm out there. I wondered what might
be on the weekly news, who was doing what to whom in world
events, but let it go. I folded my cocktail napkin. Talk about the
weather? I didn't like the cold in Syracuse either. Then I said,
"Dad, you know how sometimes the weather can make us feel
gloomy, or it can make us feel good? Like when the sun is up and
shining outside?"

"No need to say, 'you know.'"

My shoulders sank. I didn't know what to say about the game
because I didn't follow basketball. Dad seemed so much more

impressed with Philippe, the bartender, than with me. Nemec Hall, I thought. It was his Hall, not mine. What could I say to impress him or to please him? Or just to make conversation? I felt a flash of anger. And I observed that anger in my body. I tried to recall the words of a friend from a cassette tape, *A living being cannot afford to live with emotions.* If this were true, what could it mean to me now? I tried to focus on the scoreboard of the Syracuse basketball game. Anger was an emotion. Fear, guilt, and insecurity, were all emotions and highly destructive to the body. Unlike feelings, they could tear a body apart. Storms could tear a city apart. I couldn't afford to live with emotions. Especially now. Not on a visit. Emotions carry violent electrical energy, I thought, the same as storms.

I tried to let it pass.

Besides, Dad would never get my oddball notion that just as we can feel good because of a wonderfully bright and sunny day out-of-doors, the weather can feel good because of us! He'd never get that rough weather patterns were simply the earth's way of balancing the stress of human events, just like rough emotional patterns were the body's way of balancing the stress of human life. Never in a million years. After having worked on so many bodies, it made sense, but what would I say to him and what would it matter? Maybe it was just another storm out there.

"Dad, do you think there's a relationship between what people do and what the weather does?"

"Don't mumble."

This was going nowhere. I sat back and observed my trying to try to stop my emotional reacting. Maybe the only problem was that I was calling it "my" emotional reacting, instead of "the" emotional reacting. When I would take a moment to look into it, it was always as if it was something happening to "me," or at "me", and not *me* at all. And was there, after all, any problem? I was now seated in one of the finest hotels in the United States with superb one-on-one service and my brain was going a million miles a minute! After a few moments, I looked around. Interesting place, I thought. Wouldn't want to live here.

An attractive couple entered hand-in-hand and made an easy right turn to the tables. They seemed content. The woman was blonde and looked like a client of mine in L.A. who over the years had become a friend. This often happens. Her name was Tally. I remembered how I'd once gone to see a movie with Tally and with her boyfriend. They worked together in the high stress movie industry on a daily basis. The movie starred a mutual friend of ours but it wasn't all that good. Tally fell asleep in her chair. What amazed me that evening was how harmonious this couple was. Each movement they made was the essence of peace. To see them take their seats just in the movie theater was like watching a dance. I thought then, if everyone lived with such care and attention to themselves and to each other, it would be a different world. Emotions would be properly processed and pass harmlessly away. I hadn't had the same luck in my recent romantic relationships as Tally. I was supposed to be the "healer", but my relationships before and after massage school weren't very healing for me. Later, while on a visit to the well kept home of this very aware woman, I couldn't help but ask, "What's your secret?" She said, simply, "We know we can argue, we know we can rack up points, and we choose not to."

That takes awareness and self discipline, I thought. I smiled to Philippe. He seemed nice enough. I wouldn't pound on him.

It didn't matter if my words weren't about to make any sense.

"Sorry, but there wouldn't be anything linear about it. It would be more a cycle, you know? Or a spiral. Weather isn't a linear thing. You know what linear is? Linear, okay, *linear* is the length of this bar, all the way down there. It's the bullet shot out of the barrel of your 12 gauge shotgun, and my old 4:10. *Linear* is the barrel. There's nothing linear in nature."

"So?"

"So Dad, there's research out there that says that weather patterns and emotions are made up of the same stuff, the same energy, electrical energy." He wasn't listening or didn't seem to be. I'd have to take a different tact. The linear thing didn't do it. "You know how Mom used to say how she'd feel electricity in her hands and fingers? It's invisible. And it connects us all together, this energy, this stuff of life. Like so...so just like weather patterns have energy in them and make storms, out there in the ocean, people have energy in them and...it can influence the weather." I blew out a breath. "It's all a balancing act."

"Balance."

"Yeah, so the way I see it, or have found, is that there's emotional weather patterns. Like some storms are angry, some are gentle, and some don't seem to know what to do with themselves. You can even tell what kind by the feeling in your guts. Same with people. I mean, some are angry, some are gentle...you know?"

"Don't say 'you know.' If I knew, you wouldn't be telling me, would you?"

This was going to be hard.

"And there are seasons. The seasons are just seasons and need to happen, okay? They need to happen...just like digestion of our food or our breathing needs to happen, okay? But if people were serene and peaceful, just inside their own bodies, if they were more in touch with inner feelings and not just emotions, it would be good weather out there most all the time. The seasons wouldn't have to happen with such drama, hurricanes wouldn't be so...intense. Emotions cover the finer feelings up."

"What is it you're trying to say?"

"Nothing, Dad." Syracuse lost two baskets to Clemson. I

looked at the tiny fish under our hands. What if what I said was actually true? If it was, it seemed so simple, obvious. Like breathing. But no one I knew of was talking about this either. Why not? Had anyone made the connection?

I made a quick review. Just from the old man's information, I had learned to look at most so called symptoms as normal adaptations to deep emotional stress. Why "adaptations?" The body has to work hard to adapt to the many emotions, and their biochemical discharges, that we constantly dump into it, emotions of anger, guilt, fear, and insecurities of all kinds. The body is not designed to function with these few, rather destructive emotions all of the time, or we'd be fine. An acute disorder doesn't arise out of nowhere, on the instant; it can take some time for our marvelous bodies to complete the adaptation process before it appears. What's more, there is always an interval, or a lag time, between the initial emotional stressor and the appearance of the disorder or "adaptation," in the body. This interval had always been missed by those I had worked with in both the traditional and alternative medical communities. No matter. There was much more to the picture but I was talking with Dad at a million miles an hour!

"But there's always a lag time, Dad. It takes awhile for a symptom to show up in the body, just like it takes awhile for a symptom to show up in the weather, a symptom doesn't always show up right away...with the body it can take a day or a few days or a few years. The weather, same thing, same lag time. And believe it or not, it can happen with earthquakes and even tidal waves too, I mean, tsunamis, they're symptoms, you know, adaptations. One of the biggest recorded earthquakes happened in Alaska in 1946, followed by a huge tidal wave which went clear to Hawaii, one year after World War Two ended."

"World War Two?"

"Yeah, World War Two. Everybody was really happy at the end of the War so there was this big release of tension, and...and...okay, an even bigger earthquake than that one happened off the coast of Alaska in 1964, one year after Kennedy was assassinated. And Dad, they aren't symptoms..."

He nodded to the TV, grunted.

I was losing like Clemson was losing to Syracuse. I looked out at the storm. Again, I couldn't help but wonder if this low-grade storm was some kind of low-grade adaptation to some low-grade stress on a global level? I didn't know what was going on in the television news, just the basketball game. Dad pointed to his drink for a splash. Syracuse and Philippe were ahead. I wondered if the storm had anything to do with the "War on Terror," some suicide explosion in the Middle East somewhere? some atrocity? a humiliation? but that was a bit of a stretch. Then I let myself ponder a most peculiar calibration. The Iraq war started more than a year ago, in the Spring of 2003. Two of the largest solar flares ever recorded on the sun happened later that Fall. I almost laughed out loud. No way would I mention that to Dad. "So yeah, it's all a balancing act. It's all an adaptation."

He grunted.

"Like you and me, we go through adaptations...."

"Yes, we do."

I had no idea what I was really trying to say to him. I played with the red and white straw in my glass, moved the ice around. Philippe looked over at us. I was fine. I thought of the Asian action movies I'd seen, *Hero* with Jet Li, and *Crouching Tiger, Hidden Dragon,* with Chow Yun-Fat, that understood this idea but expressed it in lyrical imagery. There was always a sudden wind or storm that backgrounded the martial arts sequences in those movies. Although a dramatic device for centuries, from the Greeks to Jet Li, we still didn't quite have the courage to admit openly that our artists might be onto something big concerning our emotions and the weather. Shakespeare understood this in his plays and turned the volume to full in *The Tempest,* his last play, with the Magi Prospero commanding the very elements to do his bidding. Could we be the masters of our weather? Much more, of our moods? Of our own inner state of being?

Dad looked down at his hands. I wanted to tell him how beautiful his hands were, I wanted to express appreciation for those hands. Those hands could hold the ripped bottoms of oceans. They could hold my own hands in their soft and abiding warmth and tell me everything was okay.

"So there's always a lag time, you know? Like with any symptom, a disease process can start long before it shows up, in the body, you know? And when the weather is sick or feels sick, it's because we have made it so, you know?'

"Don't say 'you know.'"

Again.

I sipped my water through the straw, bent the straw. Syracuse scored two more points and climbed even further ahead. I'd give him my best shot. Here goes nothing. "Okay. And when the dinosaurs were around everything fell apart because of their continual reptilian violence. They pulled all that destruction on them down from above, and it was just to balance the...the flow of things. Like draws like, you know? Who knows what dinosaur weather was like? I'm sure it wasn't all sunshine and roses. It's connected, it's all connected." He wasn't listening at all. I was just going on. I sipped the end of my water, bent the straw almost out of recognition.

"I'm proud of you," he said.

"What for? What does that mean when somebody says they're proud of you? The sisters always say that."

"The osteopath."

I felt a chill. I didn't know if I was up for this. I imagined she'd been to years of medical school and been at this game a lot longer than I had, or one like it. Somebody with credentials like that. "I don't know if I'm qualified to work on a doctor."

"Doctor or no doctor, the only qualification you need, son, is guts."

In that moment, it was almost as if the other old man were talking to me through my old man. "Thank you," I said, too moved for words.

"Let's get out of here."

"You bet."

It was raining hard when the Valet brought our car around. Dad passed him a folded dollar bill and climbed in the side. The windshield wipers were on. I got in and worked the air conditioner. I hoped I'd remember to not mention anything about weather to the osteopath. "Hoped you didn't mind my talking about the weather."

"The wind blows, the rain rains," he said.

I made the wide turn around the shimmering baroque fountain and pointed the front of the Cadillac to the road. "Like I always know when the stock market drops in New York because of the increase in seismic activity in L.A. I can feel it under my feet. That's one way of keeping track of the stock market, you know? And I can read about it in the news the next day! It's emotional weather patterns. It's all connected. It's a balance. It's just fun to wonder about, you know?"

He wasn't listening or didn't hear. He was in his Cadillac and drifting.

THE "I-DON'T-KNOW" SHELF

I opened my eyes. It was almost pitch black. My eyes adjusted to the shadow of the palm frond on my white stucco wall from the street light at the corner on North Ocean Boulevard. It looked like a long hand with moving frond fingers. I lifted myself up on one elbow to look out my bedroom window at the sky. There was an eerie calm. The stars hung like water drops over the ocean. A car with its high-beams on made the turn and disappeared from view, heading west toward the lake road. I thought about putting some sun screen on my nose for when the sun would come blasting through my bedroom windows at dawn. I pulled the collar of my T-shirt and touched a hand to my sweaty forehead. What woke me up? Nothing less than logic. If a million years ago there were only a million brave souls on the planet, there would still have been violent weather patterns happening somewhere in the world. I felt like an idiot. Did I have to mention the Dinosaurs? Dad would never respect me now. I had hoped to bond with him at the Breakers. I'd hoped our dinner together, away from all the Sisters of Mercy and with Mom gone, would work for both of us, *Father and Son, Pals Forever*.

I put my feet on the floor and went to my bedroom light switch by the door. The only illumination was from the streetlight outside. Dad's television wasn't blasting away downstairs, a good thing, but I was careful to not step too heavily so I wouldn't wake him. I went away from the door and back to the bed and turned on the bowling pin lamp on my bed stand. I'd made this lamp out of a bowling pin during summer school one year for a shop class on a lathe that was as tall as I was. It was a first for me and a last. But lathe work was something Dad could understand. He was proud of me then, at least, when I'd brought it home. Its lampshade was browned and the plastic cracked from years of sun and rain from the windows. I touched the surface of the night stand. Mom had bought me this and the other furniture for my bedroom and said it was sea captain's furniture. The night stand was made of dark wood with carved drawers and brass handles, like my desk-set and bureau dresser, but had been just under the windows and unlike the other pieces, its surface was cracked and white and sticky with salt air. I let the flat of my hand smooth the warped surface and my palm thrilled and blended with the love there, whatever it looked like.

With this subtle motion of my hand, I remembered a Buddhist story I'd heard more than once while shelving books and working the cash register at the Bodhi Tree Bookstore in Los Angeles. The very worried student goes up to the Buddhist teacher and says, "I think I've lost my mind." The teacher says, "So what? It wasn't much use anyway."

I tried to laugh.

I was naked except for my T-shirt and my balls were sweaty. I pulled at them as I went to my desk chair and sat down. "Idiot, Idiot, Idiot!" There were notes here somewhere, stuffed in the drawers, in my journal. I had them on pieces of paper. "Idiot! Idiot." I opened up my desk drawer with both hands and unfolded a piece of paper I had thrown in there with lots of other pieces of paper. It was a poem I'd scribbled in black felt tip. I read it aloud.

If weather had a body
If weather had a mind,
Would it be an I
Or would it be a we?

I opened another piece of paper, the *butterfly effect*. I shook
my head and glanced down, there were other pieces of paper,
and also in my other drawers, folded and crumpled like receipts
for my taxes in L.A.: *sensitive dependency on initial conditions, non-
linear dynamical systems, chaos theory*. What was this crazy feeling of certitude that I'd had? What I had attempted to explain
to Dad wasn't logical. It was mystery. Chaos theory? I didn't
know what Chaos Theory was! What business did I have scribbling down things I didn't understand on lined pieces of paper
and yellow *post-it* notes and hiding them away in my bedroom
drawers in Florida? There was the earth and there was the
weather. People were in between. The earth had had a thing going on with the weather long before there were ever people.
Where did we fit in, if at all? What was the connection, if any?
It simply wasn't logical.

I felt the inside of my legs and scratched my balls. It was as
if I was playing with myself, that's all! I felt I could masturbate
but was too ashamed with myself, felt too much an idiot! and
couldn't get in the mood. Instead, I opened another folded piece
of paper in the same felt tip marker scrawl, *Kennedy assassination,
1963. Alaska earthquake and tsunami, 1964.*

"This happened," I said aloud. "This is a fact." I folded it back
again. I'd forgotten I'd written most of these things down, or
maybe I'd repressed the memory. For days, I'd searched the Internet for correspondences not long after those clouds appeared
when my friend Kat had hurt her hand on the boat winch. I'd

thought of it after witnessing the way the dolphins seemed to en-train the very movements of the air around them, even the move-ments of the seagulls. I suspected there was some relationship. I didn't have it in the details. It felt true on an intuitive and feel-ing level but couldn't stand up to logic. It wasn't so much things were connected, it was a matter of thinking outside of my own head, outside my fear of what others would say and/or think about me, of daring to connect and make connections.

Did I have anything else on the butterfly effect? The best I could put together with the aid of three or four *post-it* notes, copied off the Internet, was that the butterfly effect was a term which described a much more technical notion in Chaos Theory, that is, *sensitive dependence on initial conditions.* It was the idea that a butterfly flapping its wings in China could eventually give rise to a tornado in South America. In other words, one small event in one part of the world could produce large variations of that same event in other parts of the world. And it didn't have to follow a logical progression and this was what Chaos Theory, according to my *post-it* notes, was about. Sort of. It was crazy, I was crazy!

"Screw this, I'm not a mad scientist! I'm a facilitator! What business is this of mine?" I dared to unfold another *post-it* note about Kennedy I held in my fingers. What if I threw all of this away? I thought. But Kennedy was a kind of breakthrough for me then.

The Kennedys had their home on the curve just south of us on North Ocean Boulevard. It's how we told people to get to our house, there was the Kennedy curve, then the straight-away along the ocean homes, then there was the Nemec curve, and if you've gone to the inlet you've gone too far. I was at Palm Beach Public in sixth grade when I got the news from my teacher that the Pres-ident had been assassinated. I didn't put two and two together that they were neighbors on the North End. I didn't know what assassination meant and I was sorry that my teacher was so upset but it was good for me because I was in detention and got out for the afternoon. My point is that historic event was something I could care about bothering to look up on the Internet late at night in Los Angeles. I'd told myself that if there was a cataclysmic event to follow the assassination of John F. Kennedy, given the lag time, then I might decide I was onto something. Or off to the looney bin with my toothbrush and comb!

Another note. I had all but forgotten the Cuban Missile Crises of 1962, an event which also deeply shocked the world. Even as a child, for those few days in October, it seemed the whole state of Florida had stopped breathing. Had the world of man ever been so close to total and complete nuclear annihilation? There are times when a sudden shock can lay over another, older shock and compound the eventual reaction to follow. Was there a connection? What did it have to do with me?

I had absolutely no relation to Alaska, anyhow, my parents had been there and brought all of us tribal gifts, totems, and souvenirs from their trip, but I'd never been there. At first, I'd Googled hurricanes in the year 1963 but then I remembered the lag time and went to 1964, 1965, 1966. I was caught up in looking for a metaphor between the health of the earth and the health of the human body, as if there were healthy weather and unhealthy weather. I'd known there was always a lag time of days, months, or years between the initial stresses that started trauma and from when it actually showed up in our bodies as a symptom, such as neuromuscular tension, post traumatic stress syndrome (PTSD), tissue cell breakdown, even disease—a feeling of not being at ease. To me, this was obvious, after all, symptoms didn't show up out of nowhere. There was something else that got the whole adaptation process started in the first place, and our precious bodies have to work hard to adapt to the symptoms in a balancing act called homeostasis.

I found Hurricane Hilda, which I'd remembered playing in as a kid, and another hurricane that year, Irma. They sounded like the names of the girls I was in grade school with. It was somewhat interesting that there was more storm activity in 1964 after decades of relative calm. That was the year after Kennedy was shot. But I'd grown up with these Hurricanes and had jumped in the ocean on a dare before most of them made landfall and these weren't dramatic enough to convince me, they weren't nearly as big as that one horrible event in Dallas, Texas, an event which changed the way the whole world was going.

Maybe my vision had been too limited. I was thinking in terms of increased hurricane activity in Florida. It seemed possible that our collective emotions could trigger natural disasters anywhere on the globe. I started to search the years that natural disasters occurred in places other than Florida and that's when I discovered the Alaskan earthquake of 1964. This earthquake was unprecedented in scope. It occurred near Valdez and was the largest recorded quake in the northern hemisphere and one of the largest known worldwide. The shaking lasted a full five minutes, and the people said it felt like an eternity. Compare this to something like the Northridge quake in 1994, where the shaking only lasted for thirty seconds. The shift in the tectonic plates caused landslides under the ocean and set up a Pacific-wide tsunami wave, the second largest recorded, which did damage to structures thousands of miles away, as far as Louisiana and Puerto Rico. It was reported the whole earth literally vibrated for several weeks after that quake.

I thought of the Back Room in Los Angeles and the way a human body subtly vibrates to the touch just after it unwinds and releases deeply held emotional tension, tension that in some cases had been buried deep in the connective tissues for years. It seemed almost as if the earth itself reacted like a human body, almost as if there were atmospheric emotional storm releases. How could this be?

It was a real stretch of the imagination but I couldn't help but wonder again: What if the earth itself had an inner core, just like we have an inner core, a core that can become out of balance? What if erratic weather was a response to this imbalance?

I hunched over and touched the finger pads of both my hands to my forehead, very lightly. I sat for a moment feeling the bones of my skull move there and the subtle feeling of the release of tension. I guess one can only know about the motion of the skull bones by one's own experience. All it takes is a very light touch. Now I was still, and wondered again, did our skull bones move just like the tectonic plates in the earth moved?

I sat with the question.

We all know that weather is a way the atmosphere around the earth works to balance itself, high pressure systems balance out low pressure systems resulting in events called hurricanes, which let off and equalize the pressure. Likewise, to stretch the metaphor a little further, it could as easily be said the human body has high pressure areas and low pressure areas throughout all of its physiological pockets and systems and that it's always working to balance itself to maintain its health. In human biology, this balancing act of the body is called homeostasis. What if there was a connection between these two magnificent balancing acts? If so, what was it?

If just this were true, was I staring at one of the best kept secrets of Mother Nature in the face? Or had I stayed up too late nights and become nutsoid?

Take one person's bad mood about a sudden assassination or a war and multiply it by several billion people. That can add up to a very bad mood. In our daily lives we expect things to go smoothly on the whole. Altogether, a sudden event like that makes for one huge feeling of disappointment that very few are going to have the capacity to acknowledge, allow, and integrate. Well, where does all this negative energy go off to, once we've got on with our lives? It doesn't go nowhere. It's got to go somewhere. What's significant is that the body has to adapt to the tremendous energies generated by the sympathetic nervous system — the fight or flight or freeze mechanism — to violent emotions and stress reactions which weren't there before. The body adapts in various ways, as observed, by neuromuscular tension, or by growing a tumor, by a feeling of dis-ease, or by blowing off steam and acting out with unusual behavior. Where does all this extra energy go off to after we've had our fun?

Before we set our too high expectation, we were feeling pretty good. And this could be the natural state of man, the way we were designed to feel: pretty good and in a state of harmony and health. Otherwise, we couldn't recognize the feeling of being in health. When we are feeling pretty good and not run around by these rather destructive emotions, we have an infinite array of feelings available to us, feelings such as confidence, enthusiasm, joy, serenity, and we can get things done in a way that is considerate of others and harmless to ourselves. Actions pass through us like ripples on the water, without leaving a trace. We are just people living our lives. Everyone can do this. It's the emotions that can cause harm, mainly, because we don't know how to deal with them. These few emotions, anger, guilt, fear, and insecurities of every kind, can build, in the individual body and in the collective body. And we all have to let off steam: World War I, World War II, Five Year Plans, purges, artificially created famines, Korea, then Israel, Baby Boomers, Vietnam, Tiananmen Square, X Generation, Rwanda, Bosnia-Sergovia, the Middle East, Iraq, Korea, etc., etc.

Now, blowing off steam is not always a bad thing, it's part of the adaptation process. Remember it's the too high expectation and the feeling of disappointment that started all this up in the first place. Of course, nobody said everything on planet Earth would be suited just to my liking when I got here, so I find it's good to say, "Don't Panic," or simply to exercise the old "so what" muscle: So what? So what? So what? And might there be a different way of seeing? Another way to live? Anyway, on an individual level, if it weren't for the adaptation process the body wouldn't survive. Even a feeling of not being at ease is a way the body works to maintain its health. We can be grateful for the adaptation process. It keeps us going. But in reality, did we remember to say "thank you" for the last invasion or assassination? I think not. Meanwhile, the butterfly flaps its wings into the dark probabilities of future generations, and their own collective emotional reactions to the same all too human stuff, all over again, and into, incidentally, the continuing rise in technology, population, hospital overcrowding, and dubious science. This leads into other very vicious cycles that very, very few are going to know how to handle appropriately. And vicious cycles within more vicious cycles. After all, the rest of us chickens haven't processed it. And there's nobody here but us chickens! What if nature somehow recycles all this extra energy through storms, earthquakes, in other words, what we see as natural disasters? Could it be that our emotions are much more powerful, and much more destructive, than we think?

"Fun stuff," I mumbled.

My eyes opened but they were dry. I looked deeper into my desk drawer, feeing all the time like an insane crab scuttling across the ocean floor. I was sure I was just selecting events to accommodate my pet hypothesis. I came across something I'd scribbled down from a fairy tale by the Brothers Grimm, *Brother and Sister.* I turned the paper over. It was a story about a brother and sister who escaped their evil stepmother and fled to the forest. They were quite alone. "...They walked over meadows, fields, and stones the entire day, and when it began to rain, the sister said, 'God and our hearts are weeping at the same time.' I'd forgot that I'd ever written this down or read this tale. I couldn't recall how the tale ended. Hopefully, in a fairy tale castle with the evil step mother boiled in oil or burned at the stake or something. I unfolded another, larger sheet of paper. Jackpot. It was a list I'd scribbled down of the dates of historical disasters followed, after a lag time, by the dates of natural disasters. It didn't appear that the natural disaster occurred first, at least for my nickel. The natural disaster always seemed to follow either the beginning of a looming human catastrophe, or the end, rarely in between.

Ends of wars, beginnings of wars. The things we do.

I squinted, trying to moisten my eyes to make out my handwriting, *Tet Offensive.* On the back of the note, the Tet Offensive, which occurred in 1968, was followed one year later by Hurricane Camille in 1969, a Category 5 Hurricane which devastated the city of New Orleans, killing 256 people and leaving thousands homeless. The Tet Offensive was a surprise attack made during a Lunar Holiday season by the North Vietnamese. It occurred near the middle of the Vietnam War. Most scholars agree that this offensive marked the end of the Vietnam War for the United States. It was possibly the worst battle of the entire conflict and its length and intensity shocked the whole world. It made a crazy kind of sense to me that a Category 5 Hurricane would appear a year or more after such an intense event, just to balance the global emotional reaction. I noticed also that the invasion of Czechoslovakia by Russia occurred in August, 1968, an event which also shocked the world.

I still felt pain over this invasion. This was surprising because I'd thought I'd processed it long ago. If we don't process our own emotional trauma, is it given to the Earth to do it for us?

My family and I were in Prague when it happened. Dad had wanted us to visit the land of his parents and look up any relatives. this small but courageous country was starting to stretch its democratic wings to put a "human face" on Moscow. It was *Prague Spring.* Dubček and Svoboda were in power and there was a mood there like nowhere else we'd felt in Europe. We found a modest apartment off Wenceslas Square for our first night, and all of us were on a high! We saw traditional Czechoslovakian folkdances and Dad and Mom let use sample the truly tasty Czech beers! The next morning we were awakened to the sound of machine gun fire. At first, we thought cars had blown out their tires. Then the mass demonstrations of students in solidarity began shouting "Dubček! Svoboda!" at Wenceslas Square and the National Museum and down the wide Boulevard. Alexander Dubček was the Statesman who had inspired the people toward freedom. He was conceived in Chicago, like Dad, and he kind of looked like Dad, but then his parents moved back to Czechoslovakia where he was born. Ludvik Svoboda was President of Czechoslovakia, and in the Czech language, "Svoboda" is the word for freedom. These mens' names were painted everywhere, even on the sides of the invading tanks in white paint! Each night there were rows of marchers with bloodied Czech flags, followed by students holding black flags. After three days of witnessing senseless gunfire, bloodshed, and the courage of the Czech students in protest, we were able to escape with a small convoy arranged by the US Embassy and an international hotel. I remember my eldest sister's prolonged and intense disappointment that the NATO Allies did not take back Czechoslovakia. She had been every-

where in the streets with the students taking pictures and record-
ing interviews. We had promised everyone we saw that America
would return and right this injustice to liberate the Czech people! Surely, there were reactions in the weather in places other
than the United States! "What's going on here?", I said aloud. I
was remembering my lessons from the people of the Czech Republic and slowly waking up again to a global perspective. I had
a curious note about the country of Iceland, one of those places
where weather was naturally erratic and unpredictable. Hurricane force winds could blow in the morning there and then vanish into sunny, calm afternoons. Was there a kind of delicate feedback loop in such places along with the added ingredient of human communities? With this added ingredient, was the weather
there all that unpredictable? I didn't know anyone from Iceland.
I didn't live there and didn't know how to gauge the weather. I
didn't know what their Holidays were, their National Days of
Mourning, or what constituted a collective emotional catastrophe for an Icelander. About all knew about the place was that it
had nice ponies! I again thought of the Czech Republic. Did the
weather only revolve around the United States? This was a phe-
nonemon that no one country could control.

Then I saw the year 1946, one of the years I'd tried to describe to Dad. I almost didn't dare to look at it. 1946 was the year
of the first great Alaskan earthquake, which was somewhat smaller than the quake of 1964, but which generated an even more
destructive tsunami, one of the largest recorded in the 20th century. The earthquake occurred near the Aleutian island chain off
Alaska, but the resulting tsunami was Pacific-wide and traveled
as far as Hilo, Hawaii, where it toppled buildings and took as
many as 159 lives. To my mind, the only major historical event
that seemed to precede it and that would have had an emotion-

al effect on a great number of people was the end of World War II in 1945. But this would have been a time of celebration for the free world! What would there have been for the earth to balance out? Most everyone would have been in a good mood, there would be champagne feelings of enthusiasm and of gratitude, people would not be all twisted up in anger or fear or other violent emotions that would release out of their bodies and blend with the electrical systems in the biosphere.

I rubbed my eyes and looked back at my windows against the dark ocean.

I again thought of my mother and how she'd always tell us kids that there was an electricity in our bodies. "Sometimes I feel there's electricity in our bodies, in my hands, can you feel it in yours?" she would often say.

We'd laugh at her. It hurts to have hurt my Mom on that. The least I could have done is humored her about it. Maybe this is what my real interest was in all this, to just be able to please my Mom now, to say, "Yeah Mom, there may be something to what you were saying about electricity in our bodies."

But she was gone. Damn it. She left too young. There wasn't time enough to let her know.

It seemed to me that hurricanes didn't have to make landfall to work out what they needed to work out. If enough people understood the way we could, with open heartedness, blend and dance with the wind and with these great storms, it seemed to me that their trajectories could be changed. But by then, the storm as a symptom has reached the acute stage. This is a challenge to treat in people too. Part of my day job is to harmlessly release a few rather destructive emotions that can arise from where they have been stored in the organs and tissues before acute inflammation sets in and surgical intervention is required. (We will visit with this amazing phenomenon in greater detail in actual case histories described in the two books following, *Touch the Ocean*.) Best to get to it before it reaches the acute stage. Anyhow, I'd heard something of this from Ada who had been assistant teaching a Craniosacral Therapy course in Puerto Rico when a serious tropical storm threatened. I asked her what she did and she said, "We all went outside and blended and we danced with the wind!" Then she playfully shouted, "Blend with the wind"! Were they onto something? The Tropical Storm passed harmlessly from the island. I again thought of my mom. For Mom, it would be a matter of prayer and of faith. It could be a simple matter of two or more agreeing that a storm would pass, and in love. No storms would be denied their needed adaptation process, but with our active and loving participation, and in faith and in love, each storm could turn from the shore and work out the mass emotion absorbed from our own error out at sea. This is how Mom would see it. Admittedly, I really liked what Ada said and did with the students, blend with the wind!

I looked for my clock. It was very, very late.

Then I thought of the untold thousands of people who had suffered after the end of World War II. Victory wasn't good news for everyone. And I saw a note on something I'd forgotten to tell Dad about, no wonder I felt like such an idiot! In 1945, at the end of World War II, horrific atomic bombs went off in Hiroshima and Nagasaki and the world held its breath. I wouldn't think it was the implosion of the atomic bombs that forced the adaptation in the weather, as horrible as that was, for there had been other atomic tests at the time, but the massive emotional reaction on a global scale to the sudden event. Nobody could have expected something like this to happen, the loss of so many innocent lives within the space of a heartbeat. The emotional energy had to go somewhere; it couldn't just go nowhere or vaporize. The world was changed forever. One war ended only to herald the beginning of the next, the Cold War. It was as if the world population was never given a chance to have its proper closure with World War II, and everyone held their breath for a very long time.

Then, of 1963, I thought of the media reports, tired clichés by now, that the world had been changed forever after the assassination of JFK.

I wished I would have said something more about this to Dad at the Breakers bar. I couldn't recall exactly what I'd said to him. It wasn't only from the release of tension due to the end of the war, not from a halcyon period global convalescence, a period where everyone could finally breathe again, it was from the collective world reaction to those two atomic blasts! I could write a book on just this subject, but what did I know? Maybe it was better I didn't.

I had some other notes I'd scribbled down from the Internet and couldn't resist and glanced at them. I looked away to the carpet. It had nubs of yellow and green and had faded in places from the intense Florida sun. Nobody would believe this. I wasn't sure if I myself believed it. Then I thought, I hope nobody ever does believe this, I didn't know if it was true myself. I pictured a think tank of important but very mad scientists in a dark room somewhere who had been tracking these relationships between emotions and weather for decades.

It seemed that people on the whole didn't like sudden attacks any more than they liked sudden weather. But was there anything in this that was truly, "sudden"?

The first note that now got my attention was the tragic attack of Pan Am Flight 103 over Lockerbie, Scotland, December 21, 1988 and only a year later, Hurricane Hugo made landfall. From my notes, the Pan Am Flight was sabotaged with a bomb planted in the forward cabin by Libyan terrorists, who thankfully were later tried and convicted, but two hundred and seventy people from twenty-one countries perished in that event. It wasn't that there weren't other sudden attacks and tragic events around the world during these two years, what was significant was the emotional reaction of the world to this one heinous event.

From my healing and emotional release work in Los Angeles, I had learned although it matters what happens to us in our daily lives, what matters much more than this is our reaction to what happens to us. Our reaction to events can be prolonged for many years and held in the body as trauma, it's our reaction that can make us or break us. Our reactions can show up in our daily life as thinking, another word for worry. Worry by itself can age our muscle tissue, organs, and our skin, and make us feel that we are old. Mankind was not designed to live with the heavier emotions of anger, guilt, fear, or insecurity, which is a feeling of being out of control of our other emotions. Like the dolphins of the sea, we are at our best in flow, motion, and in the vastness of an inner freedom. Here, when events challenge us, they flow through us without leaving a trace, much like a wave which passes on the open sea, and we can flow through them. I'm not a meteorologist, but even from my *post-it* notes, Hurricane Hugo made landfall at Charleston, South Carolina, on September 21, 1989 after making a deadly sweep of the Caribbean islands and of Puerto Rico. It was a Category 4 Hurricane (Category 5 is the most severe, with winds up to 155 miles per hour), one of the largest of its era, and wrecked havoc on the coastal areas. It took over a hundred lives in both the United States and in the Caribbean and was the costliest hurricane in U.S. history, that is, until Hurricane Andrew in 1993.

I took a closer look at those two tragic dates in history, December 21, 1988 and September 21, 1989, and was surprised at how, on the page, they somehow went together. It was odd. Kind of like the 1946 and 1964 thing that had to do with the adaptations in the weather after World War II and the Kennedy assassination. I was reading way too much into this. It had to be purely by coincidence. I'd never included the month and day in my armchair tracking of emotional storm systems, just the year. And I wasn't about to start to do that now. This was something I could put aside on the shelf and say I-DON'T-KNOW to. Call it the "I don't know" shelf.

It was late. My body was tired. Just this feeling of fatigue made more sense than anything else to me now. My body was speaking to me: I'm tired.

But I dared myself to look at yet another set of years on the jackpot page I'd written. I yawned and pulled at my ear and neck. I looked longingly at my bed. What a silly thing to do, I thought. What a silly, silly thing. I wasn't a shaman I didn't think but a man of the West. And I wasn't a mad scientist, I was just a regular guy, just a "Me." Then. What I saw on the page practically nauseated me. First, the utterly inhumane bombings of the two American Embassies in Dar es Salaam, Tanzania and in Nairobi, Kenya, both on the same day on August 7th, 1998, and then next, Hurricanes Dennis and Floyd in 1999. I shook my head. I remembered how, when I came across this odd relationship, I had searched too far ahead into the years 2000 and 2001 for any sign of an adaptation in the weather, and then had to track back to only a year later. Who was I to think like this way? These were tragic, heinous events, and I didn't care to discount their horror. What had I been trying to explain to myself? What was my purpose in this? I glanced at the folded notes on my desk, then back to my Jackpot page. Both the American Embassies suffered car bomb explosions on the same day and at the same time, 10:45 a.m. 213 people were killed with 4000 injured, most all of them passersby and shop owners in nearby buildings, all innocent souls. I recalled I was standing outside a cafe in Santa Fe at the time with a newspaper in my hands and I felt distraught. It was unimaginable in its scope. Although it may have been intended to kill American Diplomats, only a handful actually fell in the line of duty, and it was the African citizens of both countries who sustained the greatest losses and woe. This shocked the world body. I again thought of the proud people of the Czech Republic. There were other nations out there too! Nations that had suffered and become noble. Was weather the domain of any one country in the modern or the ancient world? Why hadn't anyone done any formal studies on this? Where was the research to be found? What if I were to look at this from the point of view of other countries and the bombing of other embassies, not just American? What of the bombings, invasions, wars in the Middle East, Turkey, or in Europe? Asia?

I folded and unfolded a couple more of the *post-it* notes. Then I had a most unsettling thought. If this peculiar relationship were true, could we then expect a trend would be precipitated toward more intense weather over the world in the future, over a longer span of time? I thought of the recent rise in global terrorism and it didn't appear it was going to go away soon. I wondered about the Solar Flares that happened the previous Fall, the largest ever recorded. Could our blend with nature reach into the solar system, even to the sun to spark intense flare-ups of sunspot activity, sun bursts, and solar winds? Could it be possible that our collective emotional reactions tended to process at far greater speeds nearer the apparent center of our solar system, the sun, than here on earth? This would mean that somehow solar weather and earth weather may somehow be connected with our own "inner" weather. Sobering thought. Can our emotions reach that far? How far into the solar system can our emotional reactions reach? How can this ever be measured? I shrugged my shoulders. In any case, the terrorists of the East did not fully consider the consequences of their actions on the weather itself, no more than military strategists and planners in the West. What was the way out of this? Was if for us all to connect with our feelings? Could it be that simple? I thought of the very recent car bombing in the serene and beautiful island of Bali, where so many tourists were killed suddenly while dancing in a nightclub. It was a sacrilege to that place. I considered the fabled sacredness with which the innocent Balinese treated every tree, bush, every beach of that sunshine land, garlanding all with flowers and with prayers. Would there be a backlash in the weather there? Would the storm gods unleash their total fury in that part of the world? I couldn't know.

What would happen next?

I sat back and tried to review current news events with my tired mind but only for a moment. I again placed my finger pads lightly on my forehead and again thought of our inner core and the core of the craniosacral system. I had looked into this core often enough on a professional day, had looked into it with other eyes, and knew for a fact that it was hollow. You can only know this from tracking the whisper-thin line of harmony that runs through the length of the core. I knew this would sound like a fairy tale to anyone else so I would think twice about telling anyone else. If I did, I would tell it to them as if it were a fairy tale. *Once upon a time there was a planet called Earth and it was a very good planet and a good planet is hard to find in the Universe and there were good people there and there was something called weather there too.* Weather. Hurricanes. Earthquakes. I went back to my notes. I knew from the adventures of meteorologists that the inner core of a hurricane and even of a tornado could be said to be hollow. However, around the core of a hurricane circles magnificent power, the power and the fury equal to the energy of the explosions of four hundred 20-megaton hydrogen bombs in a single day. A breath escaped my lips. The word "torment" came to mind.

Could massive Hurricanes be weather that is tormented? I couldn't help but remember the eerie sounds made by Hurricanes as they passed through town, when I was growing up, as if a thousand hungry ghosts were looking, looking, for a place to rest, a place to be forgiven and relieved of their torment, finally to be released and rest in peace.

As people have feelings the weather has feelings too? Was there really a mutual influence? A blend?

I shook my head. I didn't know.

Then my fascination asked: Is everything in nature mutual?

I took down a gift card of the planet earth I'd bought on my thirty percent discount from the bookstore, years ago, and quickly reviewed the words inside the cover by the Native North American Indian, Chief Seattle, that warned the U.S. government away from the exploitation of his native land, more for my own comfort:

> Teach your children
> what we have taught our children -
> that the earth is our mother.
> Whatever befalls the earth
> befalls the sons and daughters of the earth.
> If men spit upon the ground,
> they spit upon themselves.
>
> This we know.
> The earth does not belong to us,
> we belong to the earth.
> This we know.
> All things are connected

like the blood which unites one family.
All things are connected.

Whatever befalls the earth
befalls the sons and daughters of the earth.
We did not weave the web of life,
we are merely a strand in it.
Whatever we do to the web,
we do to ourselves.

Shit! Was I right?

I had scribbled a tiny note on a lime green colored *post-it* note about a highly erratic hurricane called, Dennis, which had become a tropical storm by the time it made landfall in North Carolina, but was strong enough in intensity to ravage the coast. Both Dennis and Floyd had originated from the winds off of Africa, as Hurricanes often do, and both were described in the news as having delivered a one-two punch to North Carolina in September of 1999. Dennis came first, and days after its torrential rains subsided, Floyd made landfall at Cape Fear. I'd always thought that an interesting sounding place for a Hurricane to make landfall. Although Floyd was a Category 4 storm and had dropped down to a Category 3 when it landed, it was tremendous in diameter with states as far north as New Jersey and Connecticut calling for the evacuation of homes. It took fifty-five lives and left thousands homeless. But most of the deaths occurred after the rains and winds had stopped. The rivers and creeks of eastern North Carolina had already risen from the rains of Dennis, and then again from the rains of Hurricane Floyd, but no one knew. Suddenly, flood waters swept through towns, sewage plants and livestock farms, killing animals and contaminating the water supply in that whole area with warnings of disease posted about exposure to the water. The flood was labeled a 500 year flood, meaning that a flood of that intensity only occurs once every 500 years.

I sat amazed. If there was no connection between the bombings of the two Embassies in Africa, and only a year later, the one-two punch of Hurricanes Dennis and Floyd, if this was all a matter of coincidence, was it any of my business to know about? Perhaps some mysteries were better left alone, as mysteries. I had been juiced on the feeling of it. About all I knew from my work in massage therapy and in craniosacral was that whenever there was an acute symptom, an adaptation, something underneath had taken a long time to stew and brew before rising up to the surface. Now, I couldn't tell if this was true or false, right or wrong, and I wasn't going to defend it outright to anyone. All I knew was how much I really did not know. I'd just have to make that "I don't know" shelf a little bigger, and put these *post-it notes* up there too for as long as they needed to be up there! Maybe the proper information in the proper time, place, and circumstances would arise when I could take them back down and look at them!

I had to go to bed. But I had one more tiny note to look at, the note about Hurricane Andrew. There was a record calm season from 1991 to 1994. This was interesting. Calm. What was going on in world events, then, that a record low season of calm would develop for us? It seemed it was the time that the world could let out its breath. It had been holding and holding it in ever since the end of World War II, a dreadful war that the world hadn't seemed to fully recover from, if only to look at the weather patterns. Now, from 1991 to 1994, the world learned it could calm and breathe.

One year before this record calm season, in 1989, naturally given the lag time between events, more than a million stout hearted Chinese came up against the ruling elite in Tiananmen Square and this heralded the beginning of democracy in China.

Also, the early 1990's marked the years of the Velvet Revolution in the Czech Republic, the collapse of the Soviet Union, and the end of the Cold War. It seemed this would have had to be a time where people around the world were, on the whole, in a "record" good mood!

The calm storm season was attributed to a prolonged warming in the Pacific which led to extremely low tropical storm and hurricane activity in the Atlantic Ocean. There were only three or four hurricanes in these few years, an extremely rare occurrence according to the best reports, and the worst of these was Hurricane Andrew in 1992, one of the costliest natural disasters in U.S. history. It made landfall south of Miami and claimed sixty lives with catastrophic property damage. It was a Category 4 hurricane and came out of nowhere. Or did it really come out of nowhere?

Another note: In 1991 was the end of the Gulf War.

Wind from my window took pieces of paper and blew them around. One post-it note fell to the carpet. I tried to grab it back but let it fall. My brain started to go on total overload. The Gulf War? Come on! Surely there were other events that year! These balancing acts the weather performed didn't merely occur in the Northern Hemisphere but could show up in Europe, Japan, South America, anywhere in the world. Unknown thousands die and are left homeless each year in unpredictable natural disasters, each hemisphere with its challenges. Hurricanes of different categories, earthquakes of different magnitudes, tornados, events so common as to remain unreported in our news, occur by the week throughout the globe. Were these ways that the Earth, like the body, worked each and every day to attain homeostasis? And no one knows when and where the butterfly will beat its wings. It seemed the truly catastrophic weather had a tendency to occur after human events too shocking for people to understand emotionally, or to assimilate, process, integrate, and finally to let go of harmlessly into the atmosphere. They tended to happen with sudden things: sudden assassinations, sudden shocks of terror, sudden military invasions, rather than with predictable or long standing atrocities that people had gotten used to or taken for granted, on the whole. I again checked my other note: The great flood in China had occurred in 1991. And again, the Chinese people saw the flooding as a hopeful foretelling of democracy there. The body often has to work hardest at throwing off trauma that occurs suddenly, unbidden, such as an accident or invasion or sudden abuse. As it can go with the body, so it can go with the weather. Sensitive Chaos. This was too vague, too personal, this couldn't be. I doubted myself again and my explanations. Could the Earth, like the body, be acknowledged to have a self corrective mechanism too? Cycles within cycles within cycles within...this was complex stuff! I could have kicked myself twice and again for thinking this way at all! Nobody thought this way. I accused myself, "What do I know about anything?" What about all the jillions of earthquakes, eruptions, hurricanes, tornados, cataclysmic floods at the creation of the world? Weather had been working to balance itself out for billions of years before human beings ever came on the scene, we'd only been here as long as a blip in that massive time span. Was it the height of arrogance to think that the earth had somehow been affected by our presence here? The height of folly to dare think that our catastrophic weather was working to balance our own collective emotional storm surges?

It was too easy to look at events that had happened and string them together in nice, cause and effect progressions. *Cause and effect.* If this were cause and effect, what was the connection? Where was the beam of light? Perhaps it was a sign of glory and like the Bible, had to be accepted on faith. It wasn't beyond logic, then again, had nothing to do with logic! I felt a space open at the base of my throat, as if it were filled with groups of stars and suns in harmony. Cause and effect didn't exist here, didn't exist at all.

Why hadn't anybody told me about this?
Who was on the question?
"What do I know?" I told myself aloud. In the 1970s, people were up in arms about Global Cooling and warning of a New Ice Age, now, people were upset about Global Warming. Maybe it was all based on suggestion after suggestion after suggestion until nobody, myself included, could muster strength enough to say "no." When would this stop? When could we take off our Sunday clothes and just be ourselves? Maybe the real challenge facing the world now was the power of suggestion! It all sounded true enough, but was it true? Everybody had their favorite explanations. Everybody had to show the way. Facts are simple, I reminded myself. Explanations are complicated. In the middle of a Category 5 hurricane, am I going to sit back and ask why in the world this happened? Or am I going to find strong shelter, failing that, get the hell out of Dodge?

Another wind, more papers blew around and fell from my desk.

The thought of describing anymore of this again to Dad at dinnertime when he got back from Homecoming, virtually turned my stomach. The weather wasn't doing anything outside now because I had a stomach ache. It was a night, hot, humid, like any other night on the ocean in South Florida. Was it all by chance? There were historical dates and natural disasters in two rows all the way down the so called Jackpot page, all the way back to the Galveston hurricane of 1900, and the sinking of the Maine in Havana Harbor in 1898, signaling the start of the Spanish American War. I looked at them all like at a bad dream. This was ridiculous. All of it. Look here, I lectured myself, Dad said he was proud of me for the work I was about to do with the osteopath. Proud! What more could a son want? Still, I was a bit nervous about the osteopath's arrival. My thoughts stopped. I breathed out, looked around. *Post-its* were everywhere. All I'd wanted to do was look at the possibility and see if there was anything here worthwhile.

Thank goodness for my "I don't know" shelf!

Then it occurred to me that at the start of each and every session, no matter the number of years of working on the body, I wonder if I can still do it, if I can pull it off, and my answer is always, I-DON'T-KNOW.*

---

* In answer to pressing questions, this book was written in 2004, and at the time, massive Hurricanes such as Katrina could only be expected—one could not know precisely when they would be activated. What is being introduced into the equation here, hopefully for debate, is the reoccurrence and likelihood of such catastrophic events.

IV

Touch the Ocean

THE CRANIAL OSTEOPATH

She arrived between hurricanes. Hurricane Charley had devastated the Southwest portion of the state, around Punta Gorda, and there were vague reports of a Frances brewing far out at sea. The Osteopath sat at the kitchen table and stared at the covered Plexiglas fruit bowl. There were three fresh and very fragrant mangos that my childhood friend, Pat, a Baptist minister now and leader of a church in Palm Beach Gardens, had left for us from a tree in own his backyard when he came around to visit and ask after Dad. I really wanted to save those bright yellow and brown mangos but she hadn't eaten since her flight. "You like mangos?"

"Yes."

I took down a blue ceramic plate from the cupboard and prepared one for her. There was some fresh squeezed orange juice in the fridge that one of my sisters had brought over. I poured her a glass and set down the plate with a paper towel and realized I wasn't sure what to say. Dad had left with my sister and I was at a loss for conversation. There was no one else and the house felt empty and I wasn't used to it empty or without the noise of somebody else around or the TV going in the kitchen but it was turned off. It wasn't like I had the professional boundary of an office or a treatment room to fall back on. I was like a deer caught in the headlights at the door between the kitchen and the parlor. I glanced into the parlor at the silver framed photograph placed on the baby grand piano of Mom and Dad walking down the aisle for their 50th wedding anniversary.

To the right of the piano was the carpeted foyer that led into the Florida room. I'd set up a working massage table in the Florida room I'd rented from a massage therapist in Lake Worth. I reminded myself, again, not to tell this woman that my mom had died in the Florida room. The built up inertia of standing at the doorway pulled me into the parlor and I turned around and skipped up the steps of the foyer to make a final check. I'd put up a calendar on the wall when you walk in that a friend had given me of dolphins just to make the place look more professional, at least, dolphinesque. Under that, the long wood table that we'd use for our great Thanksgiving Dinner celebrations with so many people who would bring over so many varieties of delicious things to eat, with my sisters singing in harmony like the Von Trapp family, had been turned and put away to face the entrance to the room. It now had an aromatherapy candle, a plain box of unflavored latex gloves I'd bought at a local pharmacy, and my notes. Music? I went down to the closet by the glass doors and looked at the few CDs I had from the office in L.A., but I couldn't figure out Dad's new CD player. It wasn't anything like the boom box I had in the back room. I thought about a call that morning I had from a married couple from Santa Barbara who were coming to L.A. the next weekend. They'd planned to do four days of sessions together. I'd never been in L.A. the same time they were in Santa Barbara, it was business and I had to confirm. It would have to be the sound of the ocean, only. I opened another window and looked back at the sheets on the massage table. I'd gotten them from the linen closet in the hallway outside my dad's bedroom. There were no crisp white sheets in the house. I hoped she wouldn't mind the floral patterns.

What was she here for, anyway? I wasn't really sure. I always went with the less I know, the better, but now I wished I knew a little bit more beforehand. Her counselor had said her client liked to swim and that she and I would be a good match. They both seemed to agree from the information on my brochure that this was called *CraniOcean*. How would I describe it if she asked? I ran through my jingle. Yes, I do intuitive bodywork and massage therapy in a fairly unique blend with craniosacral therapy, a blend called, craniocean. And not always at my dad's house. And really I'm a playwright. Is that clear as mud? Healing took me by surprise, actually, I got drafted.

Why was it so hard to accept that I was actually doing this? Didn't I see the poetry, writing, and theater, even the large color field paintings I did in my teens, as a way to heal the planet?

I caught a whiff of the musty salt of the ocean flowing through the house and hoped it wouldn't offend. There was nothing I could about this not being the Upledger Institute or a doctor's office. This was a woman with her own complementary medical practice in New York City and for all I knew, successful. Her walking wasn't impaired or anything and she could certainly eat mangos. I made a last check around the room. The sunlight came in through the aluminum framed windows, east and west sides, and bounced through the sliding glass doors at the far end. I lifted up on my toes a little to look at the ocean beyond the pool deck and the battered hedge of torn seagrape and small palm trees. The gambling ship had just left the Inlet to go out to the international waters on its daily run. I couldn't see the beach. The waves didn't look rough from here but there was a noticeable offshore breeze through the windows. I closed then opened a few of the windows, closed them again. I made a turn to go to the kitchen then froze in my steps and avoided, scampered back into the Florida room, out the glass doors, took a sharp left on the patio and headed out the red painted gate to the cabana across the street.

The sun was hot on the road. I'd have to put sunscreen on

and wear my sunhat for sure. I had an image, as I'd often had, of when Mom would go on fast walks on the beach with Dad at dawn dressed in her wide, sun splashed one piece bathing suit, how I'd put my knees up on my bed and look out my window and Mom would raise her arms and palms to the sun and go, "Wheeee!" Dad would jog along. And how she'd always point out that the light of the sun comes off the water to the shore and ends right at your very feet, no one else's, and how that meant something for each of us, how it meant we were loved. And that Jesus loves us all. And how Dad would say all religions are equally true when you look inside them. He'd been in Iran, the Sea of Oman, he knew. But all the religions always looked different on the outside, just like people always looked different on the outside. And Mom would just go, "Wheeee!" Then I noticed two white plastic lawn chairs near the edge of the water. They were from the cabana and someone from the neighborhood must have put them out there. I wanted to bring them back up off the beach but there wasn't time and I'd get my feet sandy. I just didn't like them being there because they might obstruct my client's view of the water.

She had changed from her traveling clothes in the sewing room which was to the left off the head of the kitchen stairs. It wasn't really a sewing room anymore but more a guest room now with a small bed, vanity, and air conditioner. She was seated calmly at the kitchen table in a black one piece bathing suit with flecks of violet at the shoulders, her plate still on the table and not in the sink. I poured a cup of coffee from the counter and joined her at the table with my notes, felt tipped pen at the ready.

"That was the best mango I have ever had in my life."

"Good."

"And with the fresh orange juice? What a delicious combination of foods, thank you!"

"Good," I said. "You're welcome." We were off to a good start. She had short black hair and dark eyes with a strong body and slightly olive tinted skin. She filled out a few modest forms and I had a chance to study her last name. "Karras. Is this a Greek name?"

"Yes."

"How do you like to be addressed?"

"Sophia is fine.'

"Oh, hello, okay Sophia. So...so what happens to bring you down here? You've checked in at a hotel and are here at the house. Can you tell me just a little?"

"I've had a chronic tightness in my ears which seems to go down to my waist and knees. It's been diagnosed as...."

"Excuse me, less I know the better."

"Oh."

"If you don't mind, I'd like to take any of this information from the intelligence of the body itself."

"Sure," she said. "I think I know what you mean. I just haven't felt very..."

"You don't have to say anything if you don't want to. The body can show us."

"Actually, I kind of like that."

"You do?"

"Yeah."

I was surprised. I thought of something the old man from Northern California might possibly have said. "Ever heard a diagnosis is the worst thing for your health? That, and an unhappy domestic or work situation?"

"Makes sense!"

"Anything else?"

"I'm not sure what to say."

"Just generally. What draws you down here?"

"What can I say? I like the ocean a lot. New York feels cramped to me. I feel closed in. I just wanted to get away and this was as good a reason as any." She hesitated. "I haven't felt supported in my life, not in my personal relationships. And I'm always constipated. For years."

"Okay, that's enough. And thank you. Now, I'm going to do my best to forget all that, okay?"

"Sure," she said, unsure.

She seemed to feel very alone in this moment. "Just know while you're here you're completely welcome here. Our house is yours. You have the run of the house. Showers, fridge, everything." I thought of what my Dad would say. "Would you like a tour?"

She smiled, "No, not now. I can find my way around."

"Cool." I felt at a loss. I looked at her form. "By the way, it just says Osteopath here, what kind of Osteopath are you?"

"Primarily? Cranial Osteopath."

"Wonderful...wonderful."

We would start with a brief check-through on the massage table in the Florida room before going across to the ocean. She lay down in her bathing suit and looked at the ceiling before closing her eyes. I found an upholstered chair from Mom's parlor.

I sat in the moment before.

A light breeze was coming in through the few windows I'd left opened on either side of the room. I looked at the worries and fears I'd had about her background and credentials until they seemed to dissolve. I felt a sense of invitation to begin and stepped from the chair. I fit my hands inside the softly transparent blue hands which happened to be just off the edges of her feet, and scanned, or arced, the energy field surrounding her body. And she looked perfectly fine.

I'm often asked about *arcing*. Carolyn Myss calls it "scanning,"

John Upledger calls it "arcing," Spiritual Healers call it what they call it. What's in a name? It's a way of finding energy blockages in the body so we can know what to treat. There are energy blockages in the physical body and there are energy blockages in the energy body and yet both are intimately related to each other. Different practitioners will often find different blockages since each practitioner, as simple as it may seem, is different and has a different talent and point of view, and, on the other hand, different practitioners will very often zero in on the same blockage. This is done without words spoken aloud and, as properly applied in the art of craniosacral therapy, without asking the client or patient beforehand where it hurts.

I wondered what she was doing here. I could tell she'd had good osteopathic work. There was a nice structural alignment to her tissues, all well done, although it did somehow seem too aligned, too tight. Maybe we'd need to make it looser and sloppier and get it flowing? I didn't know. "I can feel that in my head," she said, with some discomfort. This surprised me. Is there something I was missing? I stood back and arced again, refocused on the blue hands: Time itself seemed to slow down almost to a stop and expand. I now felt grateful for all the lessons from my formal training in craniosacral and massage and also for all I'd had the privilege to discover on my own. There was more than a casual inspection allowed and required more concentration on my part, for again there were appearing those dark lines, what I'd often call for my thumbnail reference, lines of resistance, that branched in odd directions like the branches of a dark tree going up through her legs and thighs and a kind of dark congestion of these lines coming together inside her pelvic area. Above her pelvis, a much lighter line emerged, almost a line of harmony, but it ran up toward her head just to the side of her core, the right side, as if displaced, and it stopped at the base of her throat. "Tight," I thought. Yet other dark lines came up through the center of her arms and stopped at her shoulders, and at her heart, a small but very dark shadow. There was more, around her face was a mask, as it were, of several dark lines of resistance going in different directions almost like the lead that binds stained glass. Some of these lines intersected with thicker lines in her ears, but the mask seemed centimeters above her face. "Fragile," I thought. Part of her energy body wafted off like a phantom to the right, beyond the crown of her head, as if floating in darkness. But with all this, at her forehead was a hint of a little blue flower, faintly luminous. This told me that this woman had done a lot of work on herself, inner work, but had somehow lost her way. She wasn't connected up together, wasn't in hookup and in harmony.

I thought of the planet Earth. What would it be like to attune with the harmony of the planet instead of the chaos and conflict? Well, where was the Earth in conflict with itself? The human species seemed to be in a great deal of conflict, with complaint on top of complaint, all contributing to what? More of the same? But the feeling of harmony was always here and available to us too, just ripe for the attunement! I glanced up and around the Florida room. There was enough Harmony here in this room, in this moment. More than enough.

"The Harmony," I thought.

I gave out a sigh, I hoped not too loud. I was on the clock. The story her body had to tell was all in the lines. For me, this morning, it meant that I was going to get to put some work effort into these sessions and to stay awake. It was not my place to say anything aloud about the lines to her, rather it was for her to make any discoveries for herself.

My fingers gently alighted at the top of her feet. I heard a standard speech arising from within. Why not? It might make the job a little bit easier for us both. Besides, it would be courteous.

"Sometimes when I work, I'm in touch with the body on a non-verbal level, without words, is that all right with you?"

"Sure," she smiled. She already seemed deeply relaxed, almost in an altered state.

"I just find it's simple good manners to ask."

"Thank you."

I felt grateful I'd asked because I know what bad manners I can have, in potential, and her saying 'thank you' felt almost as good as the compliment about the mango. But I wasn't in the business of receiving compliments and my holding onto the warm fuzzy feeling could trip me up. "That's the last time you'll hear that." I went around to her head. Some of the lines were caught around her ears. It was as if her very brain asked for more room, more space. "May I put my hands under your head?" She smiled and nodded. I pulled Mom's chair over and after a few minutes of doing nothing, felt another standard speech of mine coming on. But this time, I wasn't sure if it was appropriate to voice. I waited. If the words connected in through my physical body to say it, I would. I looked up at the silvery sparkles on the ceiling and the way they reflected the light. Mom had the sparkles sprayed on because it reminded her of heaven. I looked at the valences of pink and light green which spanned either side of the room. Then I looked over at the center of the room. I waited some more. What was this woman's name? Somehow it had eluded me. Here goes. "With everybody I've worked with, I've always noticed there are two tendencies in the body. One tendency is toward, you might say, chaos, imbalance, even disorder. And this tendency doesn't like change, it wants to keep the status quo."

"The good old status quo."

I wanted to smile but cringed. She had to know about this already. Do I continue? I felt a yes in my own body. "Yes. And I call that the Chaos Part. I don't judge it, it's just a tendency."

"I'll say."

"Makes things interesting. And then there's another tendency in the body, in everybody I work on, and this tends toward, you might say, harmony, balance, even a kind of order. I find it's infinitely flexible, it doesn't mind change at all. I call this the Harmony Part. You might say it's the part of us that wants to be well and whole." The blood circulation was starting to leave my fingers. I hadn't been doing anything at her head, just letting it rest on my open hands. "So while we're working, you can bet that I'm going to be in touch with that Harmony Part. Is that okay with you? We'll both be in touch with it, together." She didn't say anything or nod but a quiet smile crossed her lips, and in that moment, a whisper-thin line of harmony, colorless, raced from her sacrum to her head. This was an opening. I had no idea how it had happened, and knew if I'd tried to make it happen, it wouldn't. I waited. Then I carefully removed my fingers from under her head, leaned back and shook out my fingers as quietly as possible. I stood up and came back around to her feet. "Sometimes it's enough just to know that this other tendency is there, this Harmony Part."

"Yes."

I sat with my hands at her feet for awhile and played with giving space to the whisper-thin line of harmony. It looped and continued up and up into the thin air, as if beyond space, beyond time, above her body and almost seemed to vanish, but with a slight tilt of her feet, back and forth, it settled back into her core. In this moment, it occurred to me that, really, there was nothing to change. All was fine with the planet, and also with everyone on it. There was no problem. There never was. There was nothing to solve in the first place. On some level, we are always aware of this. We just forget. I wondered if she forgot? Why was she here? Was she here for the fun of it? as my Mom would always say. The experience? There was nothing wrong with her, with anyone. There are certain challenges, some overwhelming, but these can be addressed appropriately. The other line of harmony I'd seen, the lighter one, was still displaced to the right side. It would fit into place in its own time. I thought of Ada. For her, it would be only the feeling coming up through her hands with none of the "visuals" and I admired that. Maybe I'd give Ada a call in Puerto Rico someday. At least, she wasn't loud like Susan was, Susan, who's yelling had gotten stuck inside the walls of my temporal bones. I then wondered, why was I thinking this? "You okay with going to the beach?"

"To the ocean? Sure."

My hands came off. "Let's go to the beach!"

I hoped she wouldn't say anything about sharks. What would I say if she said anything about sharks?

QUESTION EVERYTHING

I left her alone in the Florida room and headed through the foyer to the kitchen. I wanted to stay a little in front of her. We hadn't talked about sharks and it wasn't the kind of subject I could bring up. Some clients had said how wonderful *CraniOcean* sounded, how magical, rejuvenating, serene, how just being in the ocean must be a healing, but when it came time to go into the water, they'd refuse. Why? "Sharks," they'd say. "Okay," I'd say. "I'll see you in 6 months or a few years." And then I think, *If ever.*

What I really want to say is this: QUESTION EVERYTHING. The main thing to remember about sharks is not to go swimming when the ocean is churned up and murky because sharks have poor eyesight and can't see you very well. They don't want to bump into you or mistake you for a food source anymore than you would like to bite into a license plate or a yummy radial tire. Sharks get a bad rap. They are not so bad as the media makes them out to be. I actually like sharks and the energy they contribute to the sea. When I'm invited to work in Mountain Lakes, I can feel the loss of that energetic edge and focus. I know I'm in far greater danger from boaters, jet-skiers, and the debris tossed on the bottom of Mountain Lakes than ever I was in my life from sharks. Some people are terrified of sharks, as of the ocean, but if we look at this in a different way, somewhat askance, sharks, like dolphins, can teach us what it is to stay awake. At the same time, I won't leap into a group of sharks when they are schooling and playfully frolicking in the waves, no more than I would leap into a pod of dolphins or sea cows. It's bad manners and rather stupid. And yes, sharks can play!

There are well over 300 different species of sharks but we have been led to believe there is only one that's always looking to eat people. That's like saying there is only one kind of ocean that is beautiful. The way to make peace with the fear of sharks is not to go looking for sharks and needlessly expose yourself to danger, it is to first make peace with the sharks that swim the waters of the interior, conditioned self. (That's the self spelled with a little "s.") There are sharks of anger, guilt, fear, insecurity and they will tear the body apart. They will show no mercy for you as a living being. These inner sharks are much worse, and much more common, than an actual shark in the wild. This is the real challenge for us all: peace of mind. This doesn't mean we throw caution to the winds, and there are those times we can draw to ourselves what we fear the most.

I had a friend visiting Hawaii who didn't know he was terrified of sharks. He went on an adventure with his girlfriend to swim with whales and ended up face to face with what he called a Reef Shark. At first, it was a very large shadow far underneath the whales they were following. My friend got back into the boat and reported it to the crusty captain who offered a suggestion that my friend never forgot: If you are in the water with a reef shark, don't turn your back on it. Keep your eyes right on it. Do not turn around to get away. Back off, but do not turn around. My friend told me this story, his large eyes wide, and I couldn't help but think of the emotions.

Amazingly, the head of the tour, who'd perhaps read a few too many books on the New Age, pop psychology, and on dolphins as a love and light kind of thing, insisted that they all get back in the water, because they hadn't yet seen any dolphins! This person did not believe or acknowledge that there was a Reef Shark down below that was as large as a small whale. My friend, not wanting to offend or upset his girlfriend, or the head of the tour, put his snorkel gear and fins back on over his bald head and went back in with everyone else.

This time the shark came up from far below, approached, and zeroed in on my friend like a laser. My friend refused to turn his back on the giant. The shark's mouth was larger than my friend's torso. There was absolutely no room for judgment, or blame, in that space, only total and grounded discernment. My friend could see directly into the shark's eyes and into its soul, he said. He could feel the massive, machine-like energy deep within the creature's body. "It was nothing but a huge feeding machine," he said. My friend is originally from Russia and an intuitive bodyworker and sought after craniosacral therapist. He would know. The shark leveled at less than ten feet below the surface and increased its velocity. My friend wouldn't budge. Pay attention. Watch. Suddenly, the shark made a sharp ninety degree turn to the right and shot away into the distance below. My friend, Leonid, astonished by its agility, continued to move backwards, slowly, into the boat and to safety. Incredibly, the New Age head of the tour didn't believe any of this, and insisted that all of them get back into the water yet again! Why? No dolphins! The group scattered in various directions, but everyone stayed close to the boat. This time, as if it had had enough, the shark surfaced, broke water, and very slowly followed a young woman from Japan who had gone into a wild and screaming panic. Leonid said, "She was white, absolutely white from fear, and her face just above the water." One might note there is a difference. This was not the behavior of my friend, Leonid, and yet utterly human, all too human. The group leader caught on to what was going on! This had never happened once in years of tours! This was an absolute first! Fortunately, the old, seasoned boat captain had prepared for this eventuality, and snatched the panicking girl out of the water with both hands and into the boat and no one was hurt. Simple sightings of such sharks, even on deep water scuba dives, are very rare. The "reef shark" was following the whales and not looking for a person to munch on. People are not the food source of sharks, really. Most so called shark attacks happen by accident, and the chances of being struck by lightening are far higher. It's a real privilege and a joy to go scuba diving with professionals and to get to see a shark, any old shark. Professional Dive Masters are keenly aware of the particular territory they dive and of the sharks in that territory. No matter how large or how small, if the sharks are familiar with divers in that territory, the sharks handily avoid contact. It's then safe to dive in that area with, of course, a helping of common sense. In professional scuba diving certification classes, sharks are virtually the last thing on the list to be concerned about. First on the list, jelly fish.

To be in a place of response, rather than a place of reacting, applies as much to the experience of being in water as on land. Not too long ago, I needed to take a break from writing and went to the ocean for a refreshing swim. The sky was clear but the clouds were twisted in odd shapes and the water crappy. I hardly waited before diving in. I got caught in strong cross-currents close to shore. I couldn't swim north or south, east or west. It was as if the ocean seemed upset. I struggled. I had the briefest moment of fear. I realized I was reacting. I stopped, physically, in the water. With this, everything stopped. I found my footing on the sand, and a current spontaneously lifted me from below and placed me in a wave which carried me ever so gently to the shore, standing.

What is it to live with the absence of struggle?

I think I was more shocked, if not humbled, to realize that

that to be picked up spontaneously by a wave like this and set on the shore was available to anyone who would take a moment to remember to just stop. We can remember wherever we are. "Don't panic," as it says in the Douglas Adams book, *The Hitchhiker's Guide to the Galaxy*. The good news is that I later discovered I could be picked up by waves and playfully tossed by currents in the sea when *not* panicked, as part of a daily swim, and others could to. When we can attend to the flow of our lives, rather than let our precious bodies be run each day by the raw, unfiltered emotions and all their cousins, aunts, and uncles, things have a tendency of balancing out.

And yes, we can play and the ocean has much play in her, and much to teach us!

Beyond the appearance of the ocean and its joy!

My experience swimming in the cross-currents was very different from my friend's who had found himself face-to-face with a Great White Shark, an event almost too terrifying for him to describe. A few days later, an old Hawaiian woman told my friend that he had gone through the initiation that native Hawaiian boys had gone though for generations. To be in the water with a shark of this size was part of their native ritual. To do this, the Elders would have to search long and far through the ocean for such a shark as Leonid had encountered. Leonid confessed to her that he had never felt so alive in his life. Such events teach us, in no uncertain terms, what it is to truly pay attention and to stay awake. I could only compare his story to my experience of having to fix a flat tire for one of my ex-girlfriends on a thin shoulder of the Hollywood Freeway, at the 170 interchange, with cars speeding at eighty-plus miles an hour less than a yard behind my back! Leonid says he wouldn't trade his experience even for the world.

My friend's worst fear was of meeting up with a shark, not just any shark: The Shark. We might take a hint that to ask within, to inquire with deep concentration and keen focus, about one's own very worst fear is always, always, a very useful question!

Many of us have perhaps been following the current parental debate that when exposed to a movie, the human brain, in its naiveté, cannot distinguish the true from the false. It's been proposed that our brains take it all in as if it's really happening in the moment, image by image, and so our overworked brains could maybe use a little assist now and then? a bit of discernment? (If you've ever felt scared out of your wits during a horror picture, you are not alone!) If I may, I recall after squirming through a rather manipulative mid-1970's monster picture that I was so scared I could hardly go in the water! Later, in my bedroom, alone, I realized that I had as much fear about sharks while sitting on my warm bed as I did when I was in the ocean itself. This was irrational. I had always a healthy respect for sharks. I enjoyed watching them from my bedroom window as a child when they would school and play. I never went in the water when they were schooling, of course, but I never had such fear of them before. If I couldn't feel safe in the element of water, where else in this world could I feel safe? I loved the ocean. I didn't want my joy in the water to be overthrown by the movie industry and its relentless greed for more dollars. Somehow, although I didn't have the words for it, I chose to be in charge of my own inner state of being. I began to sit quietly with the images of the one, single, mechanical "Jaws" shark as it would arise, and without judgment. It wasn't all that long before I began to smile, then laugh! It was just the image making ability of the mind.

As it turned out in reality, my client and I shared a few words by the glass doors at the end of the Florida room, before going across to the ocean, about creatures of the deep, but that was all.

It didn't seem important. And it wasn't. It was interesting, for a moment, but not important. She had courageously traveled here to face personal challenges of much greater value and depth. One day, I hope we each may find a quiet place within where we can actually welcome the freedom and variety of the sharks of the sea, if only as another interesting species with which we share this beautiful Earth, no matter where we are located geographically, and in welcoming them, they will cease to have power over our night dreams.

Watch.

TOUCH THE OCEAN

Over the next few days we would do two sessions a day, one in the late morning, one in the late afternoon, and we would alternate between the massage table, the pool, and the ocean. As she got her things together from the sewing room, I went down the stairs from the kitchen into the basement, threw off my Levi's and dress shirt and threw on my red nylon baggies by the laundry machines. I stopped at the bottom of the stairs before going back up and looked in at the tools on the old yellow workshop bench, hammers, screwdrivers, rip saws. Some of them were on the wall for display and had belonged to my grandfather. The room was only illuminated now by the sunlight coming in through the window under the outside kitchen stairs. I stepped into the room and touched the small metal vice on the end of the bench. I thought of the arguments Dad and I used to have as he tried to teach me the proper use of this vice. "Turn it to the right to tighten it, to the right, to the right!" he'd say. I thought, arguments again, what was this about? Was it something going on with her? I went back up the stairs into the kitchen and got my scuba diver slippers off the kitchen counter. I put on the broad brimmed straw hat that fanned out to the tops of my shoulders and that I'd bought in L.A. for my first trip to the Bahamas in early September of 2001 to work with the dolphins. Underneath the brim in faded magic marker, "Nemec."

It occurred to me, for the briefest moment, there is a relationship we have to nature and the environment, and then a relationship we *think* we have.

I took off my hat and looked inside of it. What were these niggling questions about weather? Was it okay to talk about them openly with someone else, a client? But how could I, if I really didn't know, if I didn't have scientifically based answers? I tried to put such worries away. I would have to trust my own intuition with the water. I put on my hat and pulled up the canvas tie to my neck. I never felt that comfortable in this hat on dry land. All I could do was try to give myself the permission to not know and remain silent as a clam.

I'd kept her waiting too long. I met her at the end of the Florida room in a rush, and we went out the glass doors and across the road to the beach together. I had no idea of what I was going to do next and kept observing any fear I had about doing anything at all. I wondered if it was somehow a fear of the ocean? Ohmygosh! If there was this fear, I had no choice but to try and ignore it as best I could. Damn! Was it sharks? It can be so difficult to deal with your own stuff much less somebody else's stuff, but the work progresses both on the inner and on the outer at the same time. What was the source of this fear? I wondered. There is a difference between being afraid and being aware of being afraid. When the light of conscious awareness dawns in the night terrors of the conditioned self, the separate and separated self, the emotion of fear merely becomes another bit of clutter that can be ignored as a trivial, useless thing. A modicum of caution is always helpful in the ocean and to fear there is no end.

Acknowledge and ignore, I told myself. I had work to do.

The sand was hot and we had to walk a little faster in our sandals and slippers. She stopped and sat in one of the two lawn chairs at the water's edge to arrange herself and I waited for her, a little impatiently. I was ready to go in, no matter what. Sitting in the white chair, applying more sunscreen, she reminded me of my sisters and how slow they could be in getting ready to do anything. In my surfing days, or even during Holidays here with my family, I with my brothers-in-law and nephews would jump into the water and start swimming and body surfing. We would do things to the water and one by one demonstrate our prowess and good luck in catching each wave. Meanwhile, my sisters would sit at the waters edge, seldom daring to go into the water. But the ocean isn't to be conquered or controlled, it's to be met where it is. Like an autistic child, or an animal, it communicates with feeling and in silence. It is to be blended with, no matter our ability to surf, jet ski, parasail, or swim. I didn't know why I was thinking this way. Perhaps I was preparing for the session? She's not my family, I told myself, not one of my sisters, but a client.

"I'm ready," she said.

"Wait." I sat down in the other chair, aware she was as bewildered as I was about my response. I didn't know what to say or why I'd sat down, exactly. Words had left me, and when there are no words, there are no words. She settled back in her chair. I knew I would have to say something, but what? I felt my shoulders relax and breathed in the softness of the air through my nostrils. The heat was steadily rising from the sand and I felt grateful I had the scuba slippers on. Something else occurred to me, as if for the first time in my life, that the sea was wild and unpredictable. It wasn't just the front yard that I was familiar with growing up here and had often taken for granted, it was a home, another home, and we were guests here. "Could we take a moment just to ask permission?"

"I don't understand."

"Just if we could sit here for a moment. That water is a home and it's wild, it's...living. This may sound a little different, okay?

Before I work on someone, I like to ask permission. Just like when I'm on a visit to someone's home and at the door. I'll wait for a sense of invitation."

"Permission from the ocean to go in?"

"Yes." My body wasn't going anywhere. It was as if it was weighted by gravity to that chair. "I know it's a little different. Just to sit and feel the weight of our feet on the sand for a moment. No prayers or affirmations or visualizations. Just to be here and ask. Then let it go."

We both shifted slightly and sat for a few moments, but it seemed that permission had already been given. There was a certain quality of light, a certain openness, a certain sense of welcome. It occurred to me then the ocean was also a body, but a body made of water. And that the adult human body was made of about 78 percent water. It was as if our waters were meeting in a blend with each other and the ocean. I couldn't describe this in words. In craniosacral therapy, when we work and our hands make the first contact, the first gentle touch, we blend with the person and become as one.

We meld. Was this any different? Could it be possible to touch the ocean?

"Thank you," I heard myself say. I turned to the woman sitting beside me, "Ready?"

We walked into the water quietly, feet and ankles first. It was shallow, shallower than it had been since the storm. I hadn't remembered it being so shallow in the whole time I'd been here, and it was so clear I could see our toenails. The wings of a large gray Sting Ray fluttered up from the sandy floor just yards ahead of us and then gracefully curved away toward the shore, its long barbed tail flowing.

"See that?" I said.

"No," she said.

I breathed out, relieved, and said nothing. Sting Rays are painful if stepped on and quite poisonous. It's recommended by professional divers to shuffle when walking in the shallows of the ocean and in this way, you won't step directly on one. I myself don't "shuffle" unless I have to. Still, I couldn't help but wonder at the way it fluttered away from us, as if to give up the space.

"Think we'll see dolphins?" she asked.

She knew about my interest in working with dolphins. "I don't know. Sometimes they show up but usually farther out."

"I'd really like to see one."

"Well, there's the wall calendar in the Florida room."

She laughed.

I looked back toward the shore to scan for the Sting Ray and let my eye travel north toward the jetty and the Palm Beach Inlet. I became aware there might not be a wide, curving stretch of a beach like this all the way south to Key West. The North End was one of the last tracks of land to be developed here on this coral reef called Palm Beach. Jimmy Buffet's A1A passes Reef Road and makes its last curve on the island just around our house before it slopes down the hill and heads west toward the inter-coastal waterway. I stood on my toes and studied the deeper water for any sign of dolphins. I thought of the stories of people jumping off boats to swim with dolphins and instead getting thrashed by them, and I laughed. After all, if somebody jumped through the roof of my home and tried to touch me, I'd likely thrash them too!

"What is it?" she asked, fear in her voice.

"Nothing. Just thinking about...a bad joke...nothing."

I wondered what would happen if anyone came in swimming while we were in the water. I looked south once more through the heat and mist and could make out the great buttresses of the Breakers Hotel almost four miles away. When Dad passes away and the house goes on the market, would I be doing this same work near the Breakers? What would happen to the North End? I glanced at the sunlight glistening in drops off the clear surfaces of the water. I flashed on a series of images: whales, dolphins, blue fins, the great Alaska salmon, and realized they were all endangered now, especially the great blue fin tuna which has about fifteen years left, if that. The water was now about waist high, around the same height as the concrete shelf at the dolphin sanctuary.

"Freeport is just ninety miles away in that direction," I said.

"Hi, Freeport."

"And back there is Rush Limbaugh's house."

"You're kidding."

I pointed it out. "There's our house, okay? Rush's house is right there along the beach, that mausoleum looking thing. Didn't know it myself until I saw a picture of it in the New York Post."

"That guy's got some walls up."

I smiled, "For sure."

She seemed comfortable and up for an adventure. I wished the waves were a little bit calmer but there was nothing to do about it. What did the ocean owe us anyway?

I pondered how much time we had left as a species if we continued to destroy the sea and farm its creatures? Inject them with genes or whatever madness we were about now? Would our children be able to grow up with the sea and enjoy its fruits? The ocean was under no obligation to mankind. I sent out an invitation to the dolphins knowing they were out there, they're always out there, to monitor the session just as they needed to or wanted to without feeling they had to come in or do anything. Clients comfortable with dolphins had often done this from the Back Room in L.A., and somehow the dolphins would appear, that is, their energy would contribute care and comfort to the session. It doesn't matter if a dolphin is physically present to make the connection with them, what matters is the quality of the intention to do so. I made a silent request to God and to the ocean to distract any other poisonous sea creatures away from us while we worked, but the space seemed to be ours, for now, especially with the disappearance of that Sting Ray, and soon I realized we were as safe as swimmers.

"You can always stop the session, if you like. Just let me know."

She shook her head and smiled, "I've come this far...."

I put one hand on the back of her head and together we gently slid back into the water. For the briefest moment, I felt like my friend the preacher giving a baptism and smiled to myself. This was a living sanctuary. I shook off the thought and focused. I scanned the water again for any Black Tip Sharks, but oddly, there was no sign of them, not even Nurses, as if they'd just been invited away. This was unusual since they'd often come in close between storms. But this is what happens in the blend. I let my other hand move to support her at the sacrum, just as an assist to keep her afloat, and now both my hands had very light, gentle, full-hand contact with her. Her body began to move as if of its own volition. I found myself walking backwards with knees and ankles bent to accommodate the gathering pressures against my hands while being careful not to trip on the soft sand. There were no seagulls, which was unusual. I held the space for her with full-hand contact and we continued to move. With my shoulders just out of the water, the small waves began to break around her face and feel annoying. I let the feeling of my own annoyance pass though.

Soon her body started to turn around and spread into a wide arc, going toward the south this time. I held on and kept up with her, scuttling along, as she picked up speed and the reflection of the sun became bright under my eyes. One small wave after another knocked her body and face, to and fro, and at times the dark lines inside her ears loosened and shook free of her head to go who knows where? I assisted as I could at her ears, and I had all these ideas to apply a variety of cool techniques to make a release here, an adjustment there, but for the most part, it was all I could do to hold on and support her.

I let my feet walk and wander under the water where they would. I took comfort in knowing that we had asked permission to be here, that we had waited before going in, and that the ocean had invited us.

Trust.

Her body rolled to the side and her face went in the water. I had an impulse to correct this but held back. The ocean is not always face up, but rolls and spins in waves and currents, why would we be only face up when with her? She tipped back upside in the water, paused, and on we went! I could not predict where or how she would move within her trajectory and focused on calibrating the changing pressures of her body and the waves against my hands as she unwound into wide sweeping turns, as if in a wide spiral. One wave, perfectly timed with the sweeping movement of her body, washed over her face and the water ran straight up her nose. She lurched forward and coughed to clear the saltwater out, but then leaned back again into my hands. She was at rest, thankfully, for several long minutes, and rocking against the small breakers, moving nowhere. I thought of making an apology for her cough but it seemed silly. Why apologize for the ocean? Or for what the ocean does?

When we work this way in the ocean, with a high intentioned touch and with an open heartedness, we not only blend with each other's bodies, but the ocean around us blends with our bodies too. In my experience, this blend extends out to the sky around us, the clouds, even the wind, or the absence of wind, to the sun and the stars beyond. The elements welcome this and join in the blend for this is what nature can understand, this is what nature can respond to. It is a language based on cooperation, not competition, the quiet language of silence, no words, within the blend and it is glory.

The small waves kept knocking her face and neck, one way and then another, and her body started to turn to the side and go into yet another wide sweeping arc. Her body then lengthened, planed out and sped along the edge of the shore, heading north toward the house and then made a smaller sweep, closer to the moving center. The foam would splash off her face into my eyes and mouth. I would silently turn away, take care of it, refocus. I smiled to myself: This woman was nothing like handling a fiber glass hardened surfboard on the waves.

I thought of the surfing I'd done on this beach and the photos of its waves in Surfer magazines, this being one of the most sought after surf spots on the East Coast. The big rollers wouldn't be in until the next winter's season. This beach used to be called the "Nemec's" because my parents let the surfers keep their boards in the front yard and park in the driveway and take showers in the basement. My parents also set up a trampoline in the back-yard for the kids around the neighborhood who were too small to surf or not into surfing. The island of Palm Beach isn't just Seasons, celebrities, and scandals. There's always been families and a community of working professionals here too, not to defend the place. It's had its share.

We even had our own archetypical "mean" neighbor who tried to get the Town of Palm Beach to outlaw all surfing on the island. Before the measure was passed by the Town Council, my Dad started a group called, *Save Surfing*. We had bumper stickers and

T-Shirts made up and all of us ragged Palm Beach surfer-dudes went to the Town Council meeting to show our solidarity. According to the local legend, she once stole all he surfboards from our front yard and put them in her garage. She then pasted them with wallpaper and scored them with hammer and nails so they would sink! I didn't see any of this. Our family was away in Europe on vacation at the time. When we came back, my mother would have us kids pray for this woman at the dinner table and would take time out to visit with her each Christmas. Her kids were nice to the surfers and so it was hard to fathom. My mother would never stop praying for her, and after I graduated college, I actually grew to like her a little.

Some time later, I stopped surfing and went away to school. The Break has long since been named, Reef Road, after the nearest beach road to the house. Surfers come here from all over Florida, but some can get rather violent about their waves. Fights can break out on the beach between sets. We never were that way on the waves. We learned to respect the power of the ocean, especially after one of our comrades wiped out in Hawaii and drowned. He was just a little guy with sun bleached hair but a better surfer than any of us! He could ride the nose of a Florida *Holmesy* forever! We were the first group of locals to surf this Break, but we remembered our good manners when waiting for the large sets to arise from out at sea. Each new surfer was welcomed and treated respectfully, as a guest. The whole idea of surfing then was a way to open to something greater than ourselves while being in harmony with each other and the waves. It was almost spiritual, I thought.

We were cool.

Who would have known I'd be doing this now?

I mused on these ideas as I continued to hold her. Perspiration formed along the brow of my sunhat. My hands weren't about to move from where they were, I closed my eyes tightly together and quickly dunked my forehead into the water, the saltwater stinging. I'd forgotten all about lines of resistance or even lines of harmony and really needed to wipe my eyes. The waves kept knocking her about, then ever smaller waves would flap her about, here and there, as she traversed another arc of her spiral. I tried to encourage myself through the salt in my eyes. She was focused within and concentrated. The salt didn't seem to bother her. What can the body and the ocean do together if given the chance? I looked up at the sun blazing through the clear sky. This was starting to get tiresome. I began to feel fatigued. Why'd I ever come up with this brilliant idea in the first place? I'd done this in the Bahamas but that was for fun and course credit and with bunches of happy students. This was a job for real but it was the ocean's job.

I couldn't make out the time as I had no waterproof watch. I tried to figure it out by the position of the sun, but I hadn't actually done that since my surfer days. It occurred to me I'd never had my own surfboard. I'd used my sister's surfboard. It was an old Florida *Holmsey* long board, 9'11". Nothing like a living human being. There was another rush of offshore wind and a backwash of water, and the smaller waves knocked her and flapped her legs about as she rode up and down the larger waves and over again with waves coming at her from all directions. Salt water built up in the corners of her eyes and fell away.

I wondered if we were the only ones on the East Coast of the United States doing this today?

I felt some nausea pass through me and let it go. Unbelievable, I thought. How can she breathe? She was so focused, concentrated. I looked up and scanned the edge of the shoreline. The shore looks like a straight line from a distance but when we look closer, it's anything but. Who was I to say that she remain in one place the whole time? Nothing is linear in the human body, and there are no "straight lines" to be found in nature. Nature does not a straight line make, I thought. The ocean has no ideals, no standards, no measurements. It is free, wild, and freeing. It shows us what we are, in potential, and points us to our true destinies. Had I ever seen the ocean compare itself to another ocean in a mirror? I settled. I tried to get interested. This was her session to experience, not mine. It was as if the ocean had seeped down through her skin, muscles, bones, blood, fluid, lymph, salt. Another rush of offshore wind and backwash! My head felt like it was in a laundry machine! I had come out here with others on much calmer days when the ocean was still as a pond. Then it occurred to me to ask her something, and it was as if the words came up from my feet into my body. I wasn't sure of myself. The words pressed in on me as my toes found some ground on the sand, but I wasn't sure if osteopaths said anything aloud during sessions, it wasn't their style, as far as I knew. I could feel my toes let go and we started into a smaller spiral with the waves flapping her face from side to side, and as she went into a much smaller, tighter arc on her spiral, we slowed way, way down, and I heard my body say, "Could you ask if the ocean has a message for you?"

"What?" Her ears were full of water. "Did you say something?"

"Ask if the ocean has a message for you."

She stilled within herself, going deeper, and my palms softly supported her behind her shoulders and neck as we continued to slow almost to a stop.

Then she said, "Let go of control."

This was the message from the ocean? Let go of control? I wanted to make sure. "What?"

"Let go. Be who you are."

Within moments, one of my hands placed itself on her uterus, and the other at her sacrum. I held these areas very lightly. I was concerned that no one was at the house and what might happen later? But my hands weren't going anywhere. I trusted, for there was nothing else that I could do. One wave moved my upper hand, then another wave came in from a completely different direction. Her very uterus shifted under my hands and both her uterus and sacrum began to unwind, as if they'd been tightly bound together like a coiled clock spring for a very long time.

"Let go," she said again.

"Allow this," I said. I wasn't sure if she'd heard me.

What happened next, happened, make of it what you will. I kept waiting for the next knock, the next flap, the next submerge, but it was not to be. In the next minute, there was nothing like that coming at us at all. Even the offshore wind seemed to drop. We were in about the last ten minutes of the session, which came under at an hour, and the waves simply went into a calm, and softened. Before, there'd been little breakers but within moments, they'd become feather soft rollers. There were no small waves breaking around us, no flaps in her face, I couldn't understand it. I couldn't help but think, not for the first time, of Shakespeare's last play, *The Tempest,* when the Magi Prospero, in exile on his solitary island in the sea, commanded the elements to do his bidding. But this had nothing to do with "my" command, wish, or any brand of metaphysics, this happened in the blend, a grace, a response, and my brain, the brain of logic and reasoning, could not figure its way out of this! How would I describe this in my notes? Who could I tell? My head was in a box, so to speak.

Like the dolphins in the Bahamas, sea and sky had lovingly conformed to our healing intention. She rested on the water as if part of the surface of the water. Her uterus and sacrum continued to unwind between my hands and open. But there were no breakers, not around us, not one. I lifted my eyes up to get a sense

of what was going on in the ocean around us. There were the
same small breakers far to the south but to the north and around
the jetty, calm. It was a different ocean around us than it had
been the last fifty minutes or so. I noticed there was about a foot
or more depth now.

Could she have received her message as the tides began to
change? I couldn't know for sure. I calmed, nothing to do. I
became as nothing, hands invisible, all in the blend.

"Life is not a problem to be solved," I said aloud, "but a
mystery to be lived."

She didn't seem to get what I'd meant so I let it go.

We half walked, half swam to the shore. My sunhat was
drenched. A smile was on her face but it was a smile shared with
herself. We came to the sandy trough along the edge of the shore.
She was on her belly doing a slow crawl and turned to look back.
"What happened to the waves?" Then one small knocker of a wave
came up and slapped the side of her face like a hand and fell back
into the water. "Ow!" I looked around. It had come out of
nowhere. I waited. There were no more. She stood up. I tried to
make a joke but my body was filled with awe.

There is the ocean, and there is the ocean.

THE SIMPLE FEELING OF GRATITUDE

We climbed back up the beach for some water and some time alone at the house before our next session, which was to be performed on the massage table. I was pretty much following the same format here that we did with the dolphin work, morning session in the water, afternoon session on the table, with some time in between to talk and process. A psychologist had referred her, so I guessed this woman was used to doing some talking. When I had the chance, I let her know that I wasn't a psychologist or counselor and could talk with her about anything in my capacity, however, she chose not to talk and when it was time, quietly got on the table.

I sat in the moment before.

In the quietness of the moment before, I began to witness an array of thoughts, thoughts, that I would have not been aware of had I been moving quickly from one thing to another. And I felt, almost heard these words: *Vanity, vanity, all is vanity. There is nothing new under the sun.* What was this Sunday School thought? What was the source of this feeling? It was from the book of Ecclesiastes. I'd revisited this book in a poetry class in L.A. with Jack Grapes, founder of Bombshelter Press and of Onthebus, a poetry quarterly in which my poems had been published. Then the image of this woman sitting in the white lawn chair at the edge of the sea arose. It was a most restful image. Quiet. Contained. There was a difference between just jumping into the ocean and swimming, or doing something to it, and then of stopping, waiting, and asking.

"Look at what you did to the ocean. Look at what you can do." Wonderful, I thought. Now, I've got this to deal with. I was okay with it on some level, it wasn't important. But there was something missing, something in the resonance, in the tone and feeling of the suggestion: 'Look at what you did.' It was dark, almost vile.

I breathed out and glanced at the white overhead fans. There were three of them that spanned the length of the room at intervals. The light changed in the room. I looked outside and admired the beauty of the afternoon sun on the green Norfolk pines in the patio below and the way the light laid across the shiny palm fronds. I searched for the feeling of this suggestion and it was arrogance. Be gone! For of myself I do nothing. Which was another way of saying I could not take the credit for any of this, nada.

The sunlight again changed in the room. There was a bright streak of light across the carpet from the west. I wasn't about to move from the chair. Then I thought, was this feeling of arrogance hers? Or mine? I hadn't been feeling arrogance before I sat down to work, rather a sense of relief that she'd met the ocean and a feeling of gratitude for having come this far. Arrogance is a rather tricky combination of emotions. If we can attend to it, listen, it's very loud and sticks out like a sore thumb. It's not at all like the feelings of joy, confidence, enthusiasm, exhilaration, that we all have access to in our wonderful, present moment. Arrogance pretends to be a feeling. It's quite subtle. It can catch the best of us off-guard. With only the awareness that this might be her stuff, not mine, the feeling of arrogance somehow passed away from me and she made a sudden movement on the table. A space had opened. I felt cleaner and clearer in my own body. This meant to me that it was indeed hers, not mine. This is the value of "the moment before." I hadn't said anything out loud. I didn't know what the arrogance was about. It passed away from me as quickly as it had appeared. It wasn't important. Later, it would be my turn. Before beginning any kind of focused, concentrated activity, it can be somewhat useful to pay attention, get the mind quiet, and let things sort themselves out. I grounded, feeling the weight of my body on the chair. And who could know what that subtle feeling, however unpleasant, could gift to her? For me to have continued to hold onto it, as my own, would have been to steal from her a possible insight that could make a change, even a new life.

I felt a simple feeling of being in gratitude.

Then the invitation to begin.

I stood up from the chair and moved toward her feet. I lifted my palms to arc her body. Time itself slowed and expanded. There were small, slow moving swirls now, almost tiny spirals. The dark branching lines that had gone through her legs had started to turn gray and to crumble like dust, and there was now a light inside her uterus and it was bright, although quite small. The whisper-thin line of harmony that had appeared before was still in her core and on a steady hum. I guessed it would gain in wholeness and strength as our work continued. "Nice," I thought. The other, thicker line that had gone up from her pelvis was now closer to her core and it didn't seem so displaced to the right as it was before, but it still ended at the base of her throat.

I realized I had forgotten this woman's name. "What is this woman's name?" I wondered. I had drawn a blank.

There was a kind of darkness at her forehead, but her face wasn't so patterned with all those dark lines — the stained glass — many of them had broken apart, others had simply vanished, and the sense of the mask was to be no longer. I sat and remained at her feet and calibrated the flow of the whisper-thin line that continued to run up through her core. We had blended by now and were as one. The darkness at her forehead seemed to grow in intensity.

"What's going on for you now?"

"My head is tight. There's tension in my forehead."

An energy of fixing things ran through her body. "Can you allow that tension? Without trying to fix it?"

"I'll try."

"Okay, and observe any trying to fix it too."

She laughed.

That rush of energy of her trying to fix the tension in her forehead had created more tension in her body and she calmed. I felt drawn to go to her head, but after I stood up and moved forward, I tuned and slid my hands under both of her shoulder blades, perhaps to calm her even more? That motion of spirals was continuing throughout her body, possibly from the wave action, and I recalled that feeling of nausea, of sea sickness, that had surfaced for a few minutes and then dissolved. The slow swirling spirals were of different diameters, I'd never seen them before, or if I had, hadn't paid them attention.

What were these spirals?

I felt a feeling of conflict well up from my ankles. My head felt dizzy with it. It hadn't been all that easy for her to observe what was going on inside of herself without trying to fix it or change it. It's not that easy for anyone, especially in the West. and for very good reasons. But it would be hazardous to us both if I allowed myself to react to her reactions. After all, she was the client, I wasn't.

I smiled to myself.

The hardest part about stopping, or taking pause, or whatever you would like to call it, is remembering to do it.

Anyone can do it. Anyone can at least, stop. When clients have asked how they can slow down and reconnect in the middle of a busy day, I might suggest they just "stop." I'll be entering a Starbucks in a Mall, for example, or walking through a parking garage, or entering a party filled with people I don't know, and I'll just stop. I try to stand casually as possible so as not to attract attention. Now, I've gotten good enough at this tendency to notice the impulse when it arises. I may experience a sense of discomfort with the jostling people at a Mall, or the Quaaludes they seem to pump through the air conditioning vents of most Malls so you trance-out and buy and buy and buy! And so I just let my body stop. When my body stops, when I literally stop in my tracks, or take pause, *something happens.* There is a silence. It arises unbidden. It is a very safe space. It is a silence that is always here and that is not forced.

This is a very different experience than sitting in, "the moment before". We can even do it while swimming in a pool, lake, or the ocean. I'll try to practice stopping, or just taking a breather, when I go into a huge Macys, or up the steps of a Bank, or into a grocery store. Let's say there are people around who seem totally unaware of the miracle of just being alive on a beautiful planet in the Universe. Rather than react, or put down the nameless faces at the Mall, the Bank, the Party, for being ungrateful, I take a pause, stop, and in stopping, stop the emotional reaction.

When I do this, I may have the opportunity of observing the thoughts, the odd logic, the raw, unfiltered emotions going through me. And because I have stopped, just for a moment or two, then, and only then, response. And a response that is totally spontaneous, creative, life giving and alive. I may even discover that I was really the one being ungrateful in that moment of entering the Mall, not them, not the nameless faces. Not that there are any "rules" about being grateful, or even cheerful, it's more an attitude toward living.

Stopping can also be useful in personal and interpersonal relationships. For example, one of my older sisters had said something hurtful to me, something about my not being a good son to my dad. I could feel the emotions churn within me like a storm. There was emotional lightening in that storm, and I was about to lash out. I knew that I could hurt her. I knew I could turn around her hurtful words and say exactly the same thing about her. I had been a good son, stormed my emotions inside. I had been the best son that I knew how to be! I had that split-second shot of sudden awareness. I could see the pain in her eyes. She instantly regretted what she'd said because she knew she had hurt me. She didn't know it a minute before, but she knew it now. *Something happened.* I told her I loved her and meant it. It shocked both of us.

It's the awareness of what we are doing that makes the shift.

When I'm caught in reacting, there is little I can actually do.

When aware, *something happens.* This is far beyond any insistence on positive or even negative thinking. This is to shine a light.

I could write a book or pamphlet on just this. And I'm sure I'm not the only one who's stumbled across this notion of *stopping,* at least, I would hope not. At first, it was something my body would do, like a horse when faced with new fence or a freeway. There's that moment when things get confused when going into a new place, that moment of reaction, so why not take a pause? Breathe? Again, the reader may find examples in his or her own life. It's best to start with ordinary places, for example, just when walking down a sidewalk. Simply stop. If anyone notices, well, so what? It won't hurt them.

I know this is a little different for most of us. Most of us are not used to stopping, or taking an aside, almost like an actor would on the stage, and precious few of us have learned the immense pleasure and value of observing our thoughts, moment to moment. Far, far fewer are aware of their real purpose of living. It may seem hard at first, like a great effort, but once we catch on and can remember to do it, it's the essence of simplicity. It's essential if we are to find a new way of living and being on this planet. Not to mention the day when our children's-children's-children will venture forth to set up other colonies in the vast reaches of our solar system.

It's not all that hard to do.

When we can observe our thoughts, moment by moment, while at the same time, being active and contributing in the world, we may experience what it is to be, "in the world but not of it." It is beyond positive thinking or negative thinking. It is to be aware of both. It is to stop long enough to only remember. The stillness that can arise in the midst of a busy day is totally liberating. And it's nothing to be in fear of, for again, what is fear but just another raw, unfiltered emotion? There is a vast difference between the experiencing of emotion and of feeling. To be rushed through a Mall by emotion is to be driving a car with three wheels.

Why not fly?

Let's say in the Mall, I might feel the one of the few, very raw, unfiltered emotions start to react within the body and mind. There goes the emotion of anger at the people for being in the Mall, there goes the emotion of guilt for my being in a Mall in the first place, and not at a local boutique, there goes the fear of yet another huge, unknown Mall, there goes the emotion of insecurity for feeling overwhelmed by this at all, and the loss of the present moment. Because this is what the emotions do: distract us from living and being in the joy of the present.

I've been asked: Is it a matter of stopping our thoughts, one-by-one? Much easier! We all know the art of film shows us 24 frames per second. We are such that we can grasp the frames and put them together into a movie of tens of thousands of frames. That's how marvelous we are! There have been recent studies that show us to have an average of 40,000 thoughts per minute, and these studies will soon be dated. Even so, that's a lot of thoughts for anyone to stop, one by one! No, I'm not suggesting we look at each and every thought. We might bother to look at the really, really loud thoughts that bear down on us, contract our muscles, and compel our attention, major worries! Once we can see such things, feelings can arise, feelings of confidence, of joy, even serenity.

The Old Man in Northern California would say that looking at each and every thought amounts to the same thing as looking for blue trucks on a freeway. Someone doesn't sit out by the freeway and shout, "Oh, there's a blue truck, there's another blue truck, and look at that one over there!" No, they all pass by and we move on and go about our business. I for one have always appreciated that.

There are infinite ways to stop, not just by physically stopping in our tracks. It could be as simple as performing one kind action for another person each day, whether you know the person or not! Or even one kind action for an animal or pet. We each have access to a deep wellspring of infinite creativity, each and every moment. What does it feel like to stop? It's that nanosecond of standing inside someone else's shoes and finally seeing from their point of view. It's the feeling of looking at a brilliant sunset, the way it stops you, or a bright, shimmering night sky. There may be a moment of silence, even of emptiness, or wide open space.

Now, it was as if the whole Florida room had calmed down. I had stopped, and so it seemed the World had stopped.

I made a mental *post-it*: Just be aware.

The pattern of sunlight again changed in the room.

I settled even deeper into the feeling toned blending that had held and surrounded us both. I waited. She sighed form deep within her chest. I went on the alert. Nothing. I waited some more.

I recalled the last course I had taken with Dr. Upledger himself. It was entitled, *The Brain Speaks.* It happened to be held at a resort hotel across the street from an abandoned theater in Jupiter, Florida. No way, I thought. It's not my style. And I didn't feel very confident about the course title. I felt some anxiety. Would I be loyal in this moment to Dr Bob and just work on the body, or to Dr John and risk throwing the entire session? What were the rules? Then I heard Upledger's lecture voice go off inside my head, "Don't be any one technique, be all of it!" ...What does that mean? I wondered. Why be any technique at all? I could feel the reacting. Then I observed it. It fell away. Stopped. This would be the first time I'd ever applied what I'd learned in the course to an actual client situation. What the hell? If I didn't check it out, I would never know. It would be a new adventure for both of us, and "Dr. John" really did have some pretty cool ideas. I could feel my throat swallow, and my shoulders go soft, relax. Here goes, I said to myself. "Now, this might sound a little different for you, but would it be okay for me to put my hands around the back of your head and talk with...your brain?"

"Yes, I guess."

"Thank you." I slid my hands back from her shoulders and caressed the back of her head with my finger pads. Be all of it. "Hello there Brain, may I ask, what's going on with you today? Anything?"

"'Control.'"

"Control? I don't quite understand."

"It says, 'It holds control.'"

"What does that feel like for you?"

"Me or my brain?"

"Your brain."

She listened. "'Tight.'"

"Thank you for speaking, Brain. May I ask, is that the tightness around the forehead?"

"'Yes.'"

One hand went to the darkness at her forehead, at the bridge of her nose. My finger didn't touch the darkness but hovered an inch or so above it, this seemed close enough, for now. It occurred to me that my fingers were just above her pituitary gland. The pituitary gland, historically called the Master Gland, is actually about the size of a pea and connected to the much larger hypothalamus which is a chemical storehouse.

"How's your pituitary gland feeling? Can we check in with it? It has a lot to do with regulating hormones, emotional reactions. Things like that."

There was a pause.

"I don't know if I'm making this up, but it says it's angry."

"Oh, may I ask what it's angry about?"

"It works too hard, it's fatigued."

This told me this woman might not be getting the full hormonal support she needed. The pituitary gland makes and then distributes lots of hormones to the glands and organs, while the hypothalamus supports it and supplies it with the hormone-like chemicals it needs to do its job. Hormones. Glands. I thought of the small bright light at her uterus, at least, that was something.

"How long has it been feeling this way?"

"Years,'" she said, and a burst of tears fell down her cheeks.

"Does the pituitary gland feel supported by the hypothalamus?"

"'No.' No, it hasn't."

"What's going on there? Can I ask the hypothalamus?"

"Yes."

I always try to be most respectful when I talk with the brain and its parts. "Hi there, hypothalamus, have you by chance been listening to this?"

"'Yes.' It has."

"Well, wonderful. It appears the pituitary gland hasn't felt supported by you, did you know that?"

"'Yes.'"

"Hypothalamus, I know you're very busy, but you're also very, very valuable to the pituitary gland and if you aren't supporting it, it can affect the hormones and balance in the rest of the body. It can even affect...a lot. Could you take a moment to share with us what's going on?"

She said, "There is a hole. It's covered over. I see an image of a hole."

"Does the hypothalamus know about that hole that's covered over? Can you ask the hypothalamus?"

"Yes, it knows. It's hollow but covered. It's tight."

"Where is it?"

"Between them. It connects them. The infundibulum."

Why such a big word? I couldn't make it out. Then I guessed she was referring to the stalk, the infundibulum that connects the two and is just above the pituitary gland. Ohhhhh. The very small pituitary gland receives instructions and chemicals from the hypothalamus through this stalk. Could the stalk itself have tightened or been closed? I had a picture of it as hollow, like a straw. But a straw that was pinched.

"If that hole could speak, what would it say?"

She went silent and her head rolled ever so slightly to one side. "Self criticism," she said. "'Fat.' That I'm fat. 'Unworthy.'"

"Does the hypothalamus feel this way?"

"No, I don't think so."

I smiled to myself. The hypothalamus seemed too busy for any of this. "That's a lot to have in there. Does the hypothalamus feel fatigued like the pituitary does?"

"Yes."

"Could we ask the pituitary? What else does the pituitary have to say?"

"It says, 'Speak to the heart.'"

"Okay."

She said, "'Take care of me.'"

I wasn't sure who was speaking now, the brain, pituitary gland, heart. This just wasn't my thing. At the same time, I realized I was working with an osteopath whose "thing" it probably wasn't either, but this did not mean she couldn't benefit. I'd have to slow down, give it a chance. "Who?"

"The heart. It says, 'Take care of me.'"

My other hand felt drawn to her heart and there was a movement of shadows under my palm, shadows within the walls of her heart. I held back from words for a few moments. "Hello there heart, we were just speaking with the pituitary, and it said to speak to you. Is there anything more you'd like to say?"

Tears in the silence.

'Ask her name,' I heard. I'd have to get this woman's name at some point, I thought. "What's your name?"

"Sophia."

"Sophia." But she said it in a voice that seemed very unlike the proud and vital woman I'd met that morning. My fingers touched her forehead. It occurred to me to ask, "How old are you?"

"'Fourteen.'"

Sophia, as a fourteen-year-old, described the opening of the school year, and the amount of criticism she was getting for being overweight. Before dropping her off at school, her dad told her she was fat. She wished so much her dad wouldn't make fun of her. Or the kids at school.

"How does this feel in your body?"

"Claustrophobic."

I thought of the hollow of the stalk and how it had been covered over. At this point, the darkness began to shake loose from under my fingers at her forehead. It was almost as if the darkness had been a walled off "cyst" of energy. "What is the feeling of claustrophobic?"

"Fear. It's a choking fear. I can hardly breathe."

"Could it be possible to freely allow this feeling of fear? Let's not pretend it's not there."

She coughed, and coughed once more, settled back.

"Allow it."

Now, the "cyst" broke open and the shadow started to rise out of her forehead. My fingertips became like human magnets and magnetized to the shadow to help it leave. It came out in a long dark trailing line and my hand sent it away from her with a flick of the wrist. There was the slightest sound of tearful misery and mourning in the shadow as it dissolved into white light. The stalk had opened and a feeling of warmth coursed through her whole body. She rested in the peace of the moment and the sense of life renewed. But there was more. Another shadow surfaced, this time at her mouth. It was a larger shadow but somehow looser, less dense than the one before and seemed to be somehow connected to her heart. Sophia coughed. I placed my palm very gently just over her open mouth but could only take some of this shadow out, not all. It was as if we'd only taken the cap off a bottle.

We talked with other parts of the brain and slowly, gradually, a better connection occurred between her head and her heart, between the woman Sophia and the fourteen- year-old. The light down below at her uterus was absorbed by the uterine walls, and her sacrum opened, expanded in the softness of it. It made sense to me that her uterus had needed its support from the hypothalamus and the pituitary gland and was getting it now.

As I worked, just giving a finishing touch here and there, I wondered if I'd gone overboard, if I'd tried to fix her. If the body is a temple, as it says in the scriptures, how much "fixing" does it require? How much fixing does a temple require beyond its daily maintenance?

The body can do well on its own, if only given the chance. There are times when the self correcting ability of our bodies only needs encouragement, assistance, or support. I wasn't pondering now the acute puncture wound, laceration or break, which obviously require immediate surgery. Once the wound is stitched or the break is cast, it's the self-correcting ability of the body that takes over and produces the real healing. What we don't want to do is keep exposing our bodies to such hurtful traumas and harm.

The West has long been trapped in a constant struggle of cure and "fix." Each new cure is often never good enough and leads into another disappointment from the last cure, which opens the body to a vicious cycle of ever greater reaction and stress. This in turn leads to disintegration of the form, both within and without. Rather than identify with the struggle to constantly cure and fix our precious bodies, day in and day out, rather than buy into that, we can learn to leave well alone.

Do no harm applies not just to the doctor, but to us all.

Do no harm, I thought.

Some words were exchanged. She appeared to be even more in touch with herself as a fourteen-year-old in an atmosphere of mutual cooperation and care. Her body was total response.

I sat back in my chair.

I felt that simple feeling of being in gratitude in the room.

Then I had the most interesting insight. We were on our way, but not just Sophia and myself—all of us, as One. It was as if we were the Cosmos, but the Cosmos in miniature. I gave it to the mystery.

Silence.

"NO TECHNIQUES"

The next morning we sat at the kitchen table. It was a bright day and from my brief inspection on the sun deck, where I'd slept the night out, the ocean seemed even more calm. She had slept in comfort in her hotel room at the Heart of Palm Beach Hotel, and said she'd had a sandwich in her room as if sharing it with little Sophia.

"What was that like for you?" I asked.

"It was fun."

At the end of the last session, the pituitary gland asked us to speak with the pineal gland, which is much farther back than the pituitary and deep inside of the brain. The pineal gland is very much a mystery but can assist in the integration of health throughout the whole body, for us, it was a finishing touch. I asked her how she felt about what the pineal gland had said.

She searched her memory. "It said that I take care of others before I take care of myself." She paused to take this in. "It's true, I over treat my patients, not all of them, but I can go too long."

"Does this serve you?"

"I don't think so."

"And who pays the price?"

"I do. It wears me down."

"Well?"

"One of the reasons I came down here was because I've felt on burn out."

"That can happen."

A smile appeared and her hands became animated. "But last night, it was fun. It was just me, but it was like it was just the two of us, fun!"

"Great!" I was happy for her. She'd worked hard.

She bent her head slightly to one side as if listening. "I think she's just happy that I'm acknowledging her."

"How long has she gone without?"

"'Too long.'" She quieted.

The energy and atmosphere of our talk had drifted into that of a session. I could feel my body already treating her, even though we were sitting in separate chairs at the table. I can't adequately describe this. I wasn't touching her, but treating her. I was tuned in and listening to her with my whole body, listening through the words. It was too easy and kind of exciting. I'd heard of enlightened talk therapists who could do this sort of thing, and wondered, what if her talk therapist did this same thing? What if she could treat Sophia without touching her? I began to feel puffed up in my chest. A part of me, the part of me watching this scene, expanded. And I watched my thoughts from here. Wouldn't Dad be proud of me now, if he could only walk in and see me with a cranial osteopath? ...Osteopath? What was the big deal? And then I wondered, are these feelings of arrogance mine? Or hers? I searched the field that held and surrounded us both for any feelings of personal pride, arrogance, or self esteem, and lowered my head to stare at the linoleum. There was some dust still on the floor. I hadn't vacuumed it all up. These feelings were not hers, she was just having fun now. It's too easy to forget that each one worked on is an expression of Life in all its variety. What was I puffed up about? I couldn't get my head around it. What I really needed was a literary agent, I thought. I had no degree in Internal Medicine or Psychiatry. What business did I have listening and responding, like a professional? It felt shitty. I felt a drop in the mood of the room. This was wrong. I could not let it go down any further. Feelings of depression had no place here and could do massive damage. Depression is just another emotion, anger, that pretends to be a feeling. I was on the clock. I named it: Anger. All I could do was allow the unpleasant feelings to go through my body as I sat, my hands in my lap. Nothing to do but shake it off and go forward. "Well, nothing like a good time!" I said.

She laughed, "Yeah, what a concept!"

"Yeah!" I laughed. "Let's go to the beach?"

"Yeah!"

The sun was climbing toward noon and the sand was too hot for my bare feet. Sophia had left the house first and was at the water's edge in one of the lawn chairs. She was in her modest one piece black bathing suit and sunning herself with her dark sunglasses on. There were two teenage couples on the beach closer to the front of the house sitting or lying on towels and blankets with an ice chest. When I got to the chairs, Sophia said, "Perfect bodies." I didn't know what she'd meant. She nodded to the teenagers and said, "I had to take back the chairs from the perfect bodies."

"Thanks," I said. I put on my sunscreen and studied them. Both the girls were in two piece bathing suits and were stunning. The guys were pale and lanky and seemed less experienced than the girls somehow. I hoped it wouldn't get in the way of Sophia's process. What was I going to do, shoo them away? Claim this beach as my own? Our property line did go out as far as the high water mark and I could have. It was too absurd. It was only a tiny border, a property line. What ownership, what control did I have over this little piece of Mother Nature? We had let surfers use this beach ever since surfing first started in Florida in the 1960s and even the house had been pictured in Vanity Fair with the Pulitzer family from down the street holding their colorful surfboards. It was our front yard but it was also wild and living nature. Mother Nature does not respond to ownership or control, does not ask us to own her or to control her, only to be with her in harmony, only to ask. A human body is much the same way, in reality. I was grateful the teenagers were there to visit and enjoy this beautiful sky and ocean.

We sat and waited to see if there would be a sense of invitation. I had a flash of a thought about the world body and the stress it was under: There is a difference between doing something to others, and doing something with others. Why give more misery into the world? It eats into our own hearts. It hurts the world and ourselves. Why not sing a song of gladness and of joy? How to do that? Just keep up the good mood! It's not so mysterious. After all, all that anyone wants in the world, on all sides of any conflict, is to be happy. I got religious. I thought of a line from the Book of Job but couldn't remember it in full.

> Ask the very beasts, and they will teach you,
> ask the wild birds—they will tell you,
> crawling creatures will instruct you,
> fish in the sea will inform you:
> for which of them all knows not that this is
> the Eternal's way,
> in whose control lies every living soul,
> and the whole life of man.

I thought to say something but dropped it.
It wouldn't have been appropriate.
I felt the warmth of the sand under my toes. Just hours ago this same sand was under water. Today would be different than

yesterday, I thought. I looked at the shadow of the brim of my sunhat over a patch of dried brown seaweed on the soft sand. It's the kind of light brown sand that has been pounded by the ocean over millions of years so that tiny pieces of shell reflect the sunlight and looks the color of beige and transparent blue under the gentle wash of waves. The water was so calm and still it was almost eerie. Three pelicans flew down the shoreline in an easy formation, going north toward the jetty and Singer Island. I again marveled at how different this was to wait for permission. My conditioned habit was to jump in and start doing things to the ocean, splashing around and swimming, never to do something with the ocean. But on some level, I felt that either way was fine and dandy by the sea.

I looked at Sophia. We nodded our heads, yes, we were invited. We stood, and I had a sense we were on an adventure that neither of us had ever had before and certainly not with one another. The day before yesterday we were total strangers. A small wave came up to meet us. It was a little chilly on the ankles. I had another insight, as if the ocean were gifting me with intuitive flashes today. The Greek philosopher, Heraclitus, once said that you can't step in the same river twice. The same is true of the ocean. I gave it voice, "Can't step in the same ocean twice!"

She gave me a quizzical look. Then she got it, and laughed.

The ocean was at its perfect depth for this kind of work, not too shallow, not too deep. I hadn't timed the tides since my surfing days and felt great about this extra good luck. My scuba slippers bounded over the sand. We were only a few yards offshore and had just turned to face each other when she laughed again. I wondered if I'd said or done something wrong. "Look!" she said, and pointed. There was a little silvery baitfish swimming in between our bodies. It had the tiniest streak of blue in the sunlight.

She scooped it up in her palms and it spilled back in the water with a swish. It bumped between our chests, back and forth, then stayed closer to hers. "It likes you," I said.

"I like it!" she answered.

I wasn't sure about starting the session now and didn't want to shoo the fish away. This was rare. It wouldn't go away. "Well, maybe this is the session."

"I love it," she said.

She nodded that she was ready.

"Are you sure?" We both took one last look at the fish. She leaned back into my open hands and we slid down. Both my hands backed off to maintain a very light, gentle contact with her. And I enjoyed the ease of movement in my legs and feet as her body began to slowly uncoil and unwind. The water was up to my ribcage. The added relaxation I felt in not having to bend my knees and ankles gave a greater degree of flow and relaxation to her own body. There were no small breakers, only calm and easy rollers that were spaced far apart and washed on the shore with hardly a sound. The ocean was like a lake and baitfish clear. There seemed to be a kind of intelligence in the water itself, the same quality of intelligence in the water when around the dolphins. This is living, I thought to myself, and I again felt grateful for the ocean's so graciously accommodating our needs.

What is the ocean but love?

Ocean, I said to myself. Only that. And then the blend. We were once more as one, Sophia, me, and the sea.

My hands were at her liver now, the largest organ of the body next to the skin and an organ which tends to back up with the emotion of anger. I let my hands gently rock the strong ligaments around her liver, and as these ligaments began to unlock and move under her ribcage, that is, as her liver began to discover it could move freely and wasn't forever stuck in place in its solitary body

cavity, a feeling of anger began to pass through either side of my
hands, like the way the asphalt road shimmers in front of the
house after rain. Her body folded unto itself, as if in the womb,
and shook. I held the space in neutral. Neutral is an art in itself.
It's when I'm not sending any energy into the body in front of me
or taking any energy out or really doing much of anything, just
holding the space with my hands. I intentioned a very strong feeling of safety for Sophia. The shaking stopped. But there was still
a look of deepest contraction and tightness in her eyes and mouth.
"What's going on for you?"

"A flashback."

Her body shook again.

I didn't know what the flashback was and I had no sense of
invitation to ask, as much as I would have liked to. Nevertheless,
her body was releasing out something and that something was
good to release out. I thought of the few cranial osteopaths I'd met,
and how they'd insisted on not using words or letting the body
voice during sessions but would save back any releases until later to be treated by a psychologist or counselor. On the other hand,
I had been trained to treat what I would find. This meant to me
to treat what would arise in the moment before it turns into a
stale memory of a release and loses its nutrient. Sophia was a cranial osteopath, and again, I wanted to respect her process as best
I could and let go any importance I'd had about words or sharing a dialogue. Not easy for a playwright addicted to words and
in love with the rhythms, flows, resonances of words, not easy unless it's what's being asked for in the moment: no words. Because
silence is as necessary to theater as water to land.

Her legs unfolded and the strong muscles in her arms relaxed but there was still a certain tension. The sun glistened on
her face and shoulders, then, her whole body began to spontaneously spin in place, three times she went under and up and I

tried my best to follow the releases of tension and to calibrate these releases with the spin. She settled but with her face down in the water and knees slightly bent under. Dead man's float. I wondered for how long she could remain like this, without air, and I recalled the times when my own body had spun and spiraled and relaxed. For there are reserves of oxygen stored deep in our lungs that we know nothing of until we can experience their aid and assistance for ourselves. It was as if her whole body was breathing. I pictured what her body would look like from under the water.

Long minutes passed.

She lifted her head and took a gulp of air. She lowered her face again. Perhaps she was working something out. I continued to wonder at the stillness of the water and how ocean and the sky far above seemed to offer support. I remembered when I had floated like this, face down, coming up for only an occasional breath of air, and how there were times when there seemed to be no separation between the floor of the ocean, the surface of the water, the sky. I let my eyes rest on her back and shoulders while very gently cradling her for support with only my fingertips, calibrating the movements of the currents underneath. I again pictured what she would look like from under the water with the reflection of the sunlight overhead. It was almost as if there were no separation between the edges of her skin and the water. She took another gulp of air then went down again. I waited for any move she might make, any pull of connective tissue, to show that she was ready to turn around again on her back, but did not force her. Then she disappeared and stars, small suns, and full galaxies appeared within her body. She had become on the instant a vast expanse within the water. She's inside her galaxy body, I thought. It was just something I'd been seeing more and more since working with the dolphins. I didn't know how to describe this to anyone and would refrain. And I didn't know why nobody was talking about it. It seemed so obvious. Maybe they couldn't describe it either, not in proper company!

It was time to back off my energies even more and rest in the silence.

I thought back to the first time I caught a glimpse of the Galaxy Body.

After a typical swim with the dolphins at the Sanctuary Bay in Port Lucaya, photographs are taken by the trained Staff there and sold to the tourists as souvenirs. I remembered when I was asked to hug a dolphin for one of these routine photographs, bright suns of different sizes appeared through the length of the dolphin's body. Not too long after this, back in L.A., there would be those times in sessions when the body of the person I was working on would appear as a universe with stars and floating galaxies. The Galaxy Body, I'd say to myself. I would simply acknowledge it as interesting, but keep my hands focused on the session work. I had never seen it within my own body, only in the dolphins and in certain clients. I would never mention it out loud, and wouldn't now, as a matter of proper protocol. I saw it as a good thing. When it would appear, it seemed to accompany a feeling of great comfort.

Later, when at the beach or in nature, I'd remember these events, and I'd look up at the dark spaces between the stars at night and playfully imagine them as connective tissue. It's our connective tissue, or fascia, that holds our bodies together. I haven't said much about connective tissue, or fascia, in *Touch the Ocean,* but *Fascia* is largely composed of miles and miles of viscous collagen and stretchable elastin and forms our soft and hard tissue, our bones and guts, arteries and veins. If we had no fascia, our bodies would drop like puddles. For example, the way fascia was described to me in massage school in Santa Fe: If you take all the juice out of an orange with a syringe, what you are left with is the fascia of the orange. Imagine an orange without the juice. Or, if you cut into the membrane around a rib eye steak, that too is fascia. What holds it all in place up there? I'd ask myself. What's in the dark spaces between the stars? My answer would be the interconnected web of fascia holds it all together, connective tissue. Could it be said the dark spaces at night are the fascia of the stars?

This was before I'd experienced the Galaxy Body for myself. The best movie image that I can recall for this is from, *Contact,* based on the book of the same title by Carl Sagan. After a great deal of difficulty, toil and moil, the SETI astronomer, Jodie Foster, travels to a beach she has imagined in the Universe and she playfully touches a galaxy overhead with her index finger, and the galaxy makes a sudden ripple, as if on the surface of water.

I wasn't so far off. I stopped into another one of those talks by Roger Weir at the bookstore. The nice thing about this gentleman was that I always knew where he would be on Saturday mornings! He happened to mention that interstellar space, near and far, is not just empty. It looks empty, but its filled with the stuff of life, energy and matter. As he talked, I looked at the empty spaces in the meeting room. I thought of the interstitial spaces of our own physical bodies, the connective tissue spaces between our arteries and veins. I thought of the vast empty spaces in the oceans, where there are no reefs, or fish, or things to see. I would begin to look at the night sky with a very different feeling. Life is everywhere.

Not too many years after having facilitated sessions for others with the dolphins, and when it was finally my turn to float in the water, my body gently cradled by fellow facilitators, I would see more star systems, suns, floating galaxies, appear throughout my own body, so much so that I would begin to see star systems and galaxies appear even in the small fish, the Sergeant Majors, Chubs and tiny Minnows, that would swim around and pick at food left by the dolphins. How could I feel so vast and yet so empty? I wondered if my colleagues saw or felt this too, but somehow could never talk about it. I would develop a playful game of seeing all living creatures, not just people, but pelicans, seagulls, cats, dogs, even the trees and plants as star systems, just by the placing of my attention on seeing them in this way. It wasn't hard to do, just a change of attention, and I would receive a nice reminder of feeling at home in the Universe, or better yet, of feeling at home in the Cosmos, if not so much in the divided world of man. Now, when I'm floating in the ocean or in a warm pool, and at rest inside the comfort of the Galaxy Body it's fun to see the edges of my skin and the water just dissolve away into the total blend. At these times, I know I'm all there, physically, but I can't tell where my skin ends and the water begins, or where the water ends, and the Universe begins. I'm everywhere at once and just here, in the water, floating, centered. I might ask, face down, playfully listening to the sound of innumerable tiny, broken shells gently moving across the sand, Where is the center of the Universe? Am I the center of the Universe? Is everyone the center of the Universe? Are these shells? What is the purpose for our being here on this planet called Earth? What is the *real* purpose of our species and for each one of us here? Are we on track with our purpose here or way off? It could be the Universe is an outer structure, the Cosmos invisible yet infinite. The Cosmos is beyond the canopy of the stars, and yet also here, in the intimacy of the human heart, beat-by-beat. Perhaps one way into this feeling, if I may suggest, is to imagine yourself a jellyfish in the water. You can do this in a jacuzzi or in a warm pool or a warm and generous bathtub. Just float and blend. Be still. It's a really fun way to touch in with our precious bodies as one of the infinite expressions of Life itself, if you will, of the Infinite Source Energy that animates the All—in the blend.

It's quiet. Nothing to shout about or force. We see what we place a value on seeing. And we can see whatever we want to see. If I'm involved in the business of the stock market, I would see other living systems as assets or liabilities, or, if I'm into playing at politics, I would perhaps see others as voters or nonvoters, and so on. If I'm into seeing others as a unique expression of life, I would see that. If I'm into seeing the energies of auras, or the colors of auras around others, I would see that. I don't know why it happens that when I hug a dolphin and pose for a tourist photograph, I see and feel in my hands bright suns within the dolphin's body. I feel we could each discover we have a 'galaxy body,' each in our own way, especially when I remember that no matter the country, religion, race or creed, physiologically we are all composed of the same chemical elements as the stars themselves, carbon, silicon, nitrogen, oxygen, phosphorous, and more, and that stardust constantly bombards this planet and is in our food and in our water. We eat and digest the life of stars and star systems on a daily basis. And so for me, the life of the stars are a part of us, perhaps an integral part, and each one of us systems of stars, galaxies, and suns. We have no conception of what we are, of our range of influence, individually or collectively, or of our vast potential for acts of true consideration for others and kindness. The Galaxy Body is not what we are in our essence but an aspect of our physical being, much like muscle, bone, and fascia. Why do we pretend to be less than we truly are? We each have the Universe within us; we are flowers of the Cosmos. Why do we need more than we already have? When we act less than human, out of greediness and the raw violence to gain more, and to escape any and all pain, it is said the animals look down upon us in sorrow.

I'm not at all suggesting connecting with one's Galaxy Body as a technique or a method of self-improvement; it's more an awareness that this too, is possible. And who can resist the early 20th century image of Niels Bohr and Ernest Rutherford, who first described a single atom as our star system? The nucleus or center of the atom, our sun. The electrons that circle around the nucleus, our planets. Finally, I am an awareness, one tiny awareness inside a vast play of Life, of Spirit—whatever you are comfortable calling it—with the job to stay on the job, that is, to stay awake. Now, when the Galaxy Body happens to appear in a client's body, usually during an expansion of the fluids within the core of the craniosacral system—and with some clients it does happen to appear quite frequently—I just notice it from the corner of the eye, appreciate its awesome beauty and emptiness, then my attention is drawn to other matters.

At times, I would consider a passage from the Persian poet, Hafiz. Something I really liked about this ancient poet was that he was a playful rascal and would often refer to himself in his own poems, as if his poems were written from a place of witness. Hafiz does this here.

FAITHFUL LOVER

The moon came to me last night
With a sweet question

She said,

"The sun has been my faithful lover
For millions of years.

Whenever I offer my body to him

Brilliant light pours from his heart.

Thousands then notice my happiness
And delight in pointing
Toward my beauty.

Hafiz,

Is it true that our destiny
Is to turn into Light
Itself?"

And I replied,

Dear Moon,
Now that your love is maturing,
We need to sit together
Close like this more often

So I might instruct you
How to become
Who you
Are!

Who are we? What are we?
Do any of us have a fine notion of what we really are?
(What are you, Hafiz? Do you know?)
What if our blend with nature *did* reach into the spaces of
our star system? What if as a species we really did throw emotional reactions as far into space as our star, the sun, to spark intense flare-ups of sunspot activity, *sun bursts,* and violent solar
winds? What if our emotions collectively processed at greater

speeds on the sun, than here on earth? A most peculiar calibration indeed. There may be far greater consequences to man's seemingly isolated actions than we can imagine.

Her limbs struggled. I went on the alert. She went into another spin and spun back up for air and her feet dropped to the ocean floor. She gained her footing and smiled as she put her hand to her nose and blew it out. "Wow," she said. "That was really something."

"It was," I said.

She rested back into the water and I found my hand drawn to her lower abdomen, just at the left of her waist. I wondered what my hand was doing there at what is called the sigmoid colon and remembered she'd said she had years of a chronic constipation. The sigmoid colon forms the end of the descending colon on the left side of the lower abdomen and leads on down to the rectum, which is itself part of the sigmoid. A lot of stuff can get trapped among its folds and twists and turns. Her body began to unwind again, but slowly, and if I was to follow the unraveling tension patterns, I'd need to move with it. We began to travel through the water like on the day before, but without the added interference of the waves. I was facing west, toward the house, and gazed beyond the cabana at the peaked red roof and the tops of the patio chairs on the sun deck above the Florida room. I realized how close we were to where the massage table was. I thought of the old Bahamian woman, the Bahama Mamma, "We share the same storms." I looked back around to the horizon, toward the islands, and remembered that Sophia had wanted to see dolphins.

For the briefest moment, I wished I was working with her at Sanctuary Bay in Port Lucaya and not in the ocean. I caught that complaint back because I didn't want to be rude to the waters that surrounded us. Just being with another with a light touch and in the blend can be like placing hands on the surface of intelligent water. I knew that dolphins were out there, somewhere between here and the Bahamas, and that was about all I could tell her. I made a silent request that if the dolphins wanted to join us, here and now, they could. Or at least, make a contribution of energy and of love, if they were predisposed to do so. With this, my one hand moved from her waist to support her down below under her sacrum, and my other hand felt drawn to her heart. I wondered what my hands were doing here in this new position. Now, we were hardly moving through the water and there was a stillness surrounding us. It blended with the eerie stillness of the water that I had felt before. Something occurred to me. Sutherland's legendary saying: *no techniques but gentle contact.*

And it was as if Dr. William Garner Sutherland himself was here, asking me only to be still. I considered the gift of his presence a vast privilege and backed off even more from the thought of doing any techniques on her, just gentle contact. Flecks of sunlight looked like tiny stars. There was a movement of water. And another. But she wasn't moving. Her face was relaxed and her mouth slightly open. Then another movement of water, and it all seemed focused on the area of her heart. Where was this water coming from? The water itself was moving and rocking my hand over her heart. I looked around. Waves had appeared but they were not so large as to break with foam. What was moving under my hand, or, what the waves were doing with my hand as an instrument, a tool of the waves, was loosening Sophia's pericardium, or the tough connective tissue sack around the heart. Another wave, another release. Then a series of smaller waves, even more deliberate releases. The pericardium is known in acupuncture as the Heart Protector and can tighten down to protect the organ of the heart. But the heart does best when it can also enjoy its inherent feelings of circulation and flow, love and openness.

Her Galaxy Body had all but faded away, or I wasn't focused on it. It was too much fun to witness what the waves were doing in spontaneously moving my hands. Sophia's head would rock very slightly with each of the subtle wave patterns, her cheeks turning slightly this way and that, and yet another insight occurred. There are those times in sessions, when we are blended, that we begin to emanate with the other's thoughts and feelings, almost like a crystal in a radio, how it tunes into stations. At these times it's hard to know what or who is doing the processing. For me, it was as if this insight was always held here, in the wisdom body of the ocean, waiting to arise. What is it to turn the other cheek? I tried it out on myself as I held her. It seemed so simple, so easy! Generation after generation had passed without getting this simple suggestion. Each time my cheek turned I would see something else, a new surface, another vista, another point of view. I could see the ocean, then the shore, the sky, then my feet under the water. And each time I turned the other cheek; I would experience the ocean in a different way, that is, if I paid attention to my thoughts. And each new direction had its own set of thought associations!

I had tried to contemplate this for some time, but only now was it rising to the surface, so to speak. I had always felt that finishing up our business with other people, instead of making more of it, was a nice way to live.

Of course, there are some people who just don't want you to finish up your business with them, no matter how much you want to. They would rather hold onto that resentment, that anger, or emotional glitch, and demand that you change so they can be happy. This gets in the way. There's nothing to be done. Now, you are both dug in, and they are your enemy. But if I continue to see them that way, as my enemy, what will have been accomplished? Animosity is no cure for animosity. So I had one or two sisters who would only be happy if I told them I would never write about my life experiences. What harmony would there be in the family as a whole if I continued to see them as stubborn mules? Or as enemies? When would the conflict ever end because writing is part of what I do, perhaps a talent. What could I do?

I could turn the other cheek. I could see them in a different light. I had actually tried this with one of them before, it occurred to me now. Take one person, any person, or even an animal because domesticated animals can respond to this too, and just decide to see this person, or animal, in a different way for one week. Make a new decision! Let's say this person, or animal, is always indicating to you, or telling you outright, that you will never measure up to their high standard of what it is to be a human being. Turn the other cheek. Try seeing that they are interesting creatures, after all, for all God's creatures are interesting, and that they are only trying to help you, and very good at it too! They are letting you have it, so you give it up to them. It's nothing that need be spoken in words, although a kind word or encouragement is appreciated by the toughest skin. It's more an inside job, an energetic response.

They are not in your life to heckle you, they there to remind you to turn the other cheek so you can become a better person, or animal, than they are! If you do this, you will find that their attitude will change toward you! It's almost an atmospheric shift. They may possibly begin to see you as the lovely human being you'd always hoped they'd see. Why? Because the equation has now changed: Someone is no longer fighting them and that's one less person in the world they have to worry about! Now, they no longer need to help you see correctly. You can drop trying to become something to each other, stop trying to prove your worthiness, and work on just being with each other, BE! And all this from one person giving it up, not like an idiot, but as an act of considered intelligence, of conscious awareness.

You can try this at home or at the office, and a medical office is as good a place to start as any other place, not to mention a theater group!

I felt giddy in the water. This was an exciting discovery! It had always been just out of reach, just under the surface for me. It was never meant for me to be an all-out wimp, fight or flee, when confronted in my personal and interpersonal relationships, it meant, for me, to turn the other cheek, change my point of view! I felt religious today. What was going on here? All I knew was that the credit for this wisdom from the sea, I could not take. Why? I must've gotten tired supporting the releases, and maybe a little bored looking on at Sophia's face moving from side to side in the water.

One of the couples had left the beach and were rocking with each other closer to the shore and making out as they rocked. The girl, a sandy haired blonde, would sneak a look at us from time to time, and he would look too. It seemed they were trying to do what we were doing on the water but in their own way. I turned the other cheek. It was kind of synchronous and interesting and I wanted to point it out to Sophia, but recalled she didn't like them. "Could you ask if your heart has a message for you?"

She tried to lift her head above the surface of the water. "What?"

"Could you ask if your heart has a message for you? Anything it's been wanting to say?"

She settled back. "Leave the past behind. Forgive."

With this realization, the blue line of harmony shot up from her sacrum through her core and into her cranium. It was no longer displaced to one side of her core and it was luminous. She was in full alignment and hookup at the core, and any gap or break in the line at her throat was gone.

The waves backed off on my hand. I gave a silent thank you. My hands moved around to the back of her head and performed a simple release of the tight tissues at the nape of her neck, I guessed to permit more room for the line of harmony to move within the core and expand. Her elbows spread out under the water, as if lifted by the tide, and her legs dropped slowly toward the ocean floor. Her body hung there as if suspended.

"Forgive," she repeated.

I had no idea, really, of her personal history or where this was coming from. I thought of the decades of turf wars between the different schools of craniosacral and the needless pain and suffering it had caused the most excellent practitioners of all schools. There were many different schools of theater and theater training, but all managed to get along. The dark thought left me, I refocused. What could it mean, for her, to forgive? Her body continued to soak in the deep meaning of this word, forgive, meaning that was meant for only her to receive. I meanwhile backed off my touch pressure even more and played with turning the other cheek! The kids went back up to the beach to sit on their towels. The water calmed. I hadn't even planned to work on her heart this morning but somehow the ocean knew.

As her body rested in the now calm waters, I somehow thought of perspective in the art of painting and the too high standards held up to painters to depict the figure, for example, according to real life. What if the figure were floating in the ocean? What if the artist was blended with the model, and the painting allowed to unfold, moment by moment? When I would begin to paint from the human figure, long after these sessions with Sophia, I would remember this insight and take a moment to actually blend with the model in front of me. Blended, I would often chat freely with the models in the total environment of the studio class. Rather than doing something to the model, or to the canvas, there is a blend that can occur in the invisible world which makes each new painting dynamic and very alive. It was just a different way of seeing, a new perspective.

Then I heard a plane overhead, coming down from the north, from Singer Island and beyond, headed south over the wide stretch of beach. It was an old biplane and it was dragging a long commercial banner. I looked up and bothered to read the banner, slightly askance. It was advertising some local club that I was vaguely familiar with, but then it said something else. I checked in with my hands. This was too good for Sophia to miss and it might give her a smile. There was enough of a release to make room in there now, and besides, we'd been in the water a full hour for sure.

"Sophia, look up."

"Where?"

"There, at the plane."

She read the words on the banner: SEE HEART TONIGHT. "My God! See Heart Tonight?"

"Is that a name of a band?" I asked.

"Yes, I've heard of it."

She leaned back and I had no choice but to support her for a few more minutes. She was still in her blend with the ocean. Her body began to move with the water and after traveling with her for a hundred feet or so, she came to rest, found her footing, and stood.

"Looks like you're going to go night clubbing tonight!"

She was thoughtful. "No, I don't think so."

"Why not?"

"There's other ways besides clubs, sir."

"All right," I laughed, "all right."

"Little Sophia and I are going to share another sandwich in the hotel room. That will be enough."

I felt like going out to the club myself, to take a break and check out the band. I took off my big straw hat, leaned back to dunk my head and then wrangled my scuba slippers off, balancing on one leg at a time. For a moment, I thought of the little blue fish. We'd ended the session a little farther away from the house than the morning before, and as we walked toward the shore she touched her chest and she stopped. "I've never done that," she said. "I've never opened my heart before. Let it."

"Congratulations. You worked hard."

We turned back to the ocean before stepping onto the beach. We both nodded and gave a silent thank you. What else could anyone ever say to the ocean but thanks? The wind seemed to answer us. Then a sudden outburst of laughter from the teenagers.

Sophia smoldered.

"What is it?" I asked.

"Nothing. The perfect bodies. Attitude."

"They're just kids," I said. "Of course, they have attitude. Attitude is about their only...survival mechanism."

She didn't buy it.

We dropped it and walked toward the cabana, passing the kids, and I looked beyond them to old Rush Limbaugh's house, the same house that had been pictured in the *New York Daily News* the year before, the house where he'd been busted with his nurse for prescription drug abuse. Closer were the empty ruins of Aldo Gucci's broken estate, and I wondered if those two men, with all of their clothes, cars, shoes, had ever in their lives touched what this brave woman had? The ocean.

I wanted to say something more but didn't. So I turned the other cheek!

CLOSING NOTES AND FAREWELLS

We sat back with bottles of water in the patio chairs on the sun deck. We could see the variations and reflections of light on the waves as the sun set behind us in the West and over Lake Worth. I always enjoyed the sunset from the deck. I could see the tall red and white towers of Florida Power and Light beyond the rustling tops of green trees. The towers were always kind of a landmark for me on both coasts. If I was flying from Florida, or even flying from L.A., red and white candy striped towers would be one of the last things I'd see after take off.

I remembered pointing them out to a bright eyed eight-year-old boy I'd happened to be seated with on my plane ride out here this time. He took an interest in what I did and for the whole trip we talked about dolphins. Not long before landing, he pointed out the window, "Look!" I did and couldn't make out what he was so excited about. "A dolphin!" he exclaimed. His young bespeckled mom was seated in front of us and turned around to see what the commotion was. I looked out the window and saw with his eyes, a rising gray and white cloud mass in the shape of a dolphin leaping out of the ocean waves. I smiled and thought to give at least the name of my website to his mom so they could learn more, but didn't. He asked me to say hi to the dolphins for him. I said I would but it seemed they'd already said hello to him!

Then we saw the towers.

I had my notes in hand and clipboard but was thinking of clouds. What if whenever we saw a striking cloud pattern, or a shape in the clouds, what if something was going on with someone else underneath those clouds? How could we ever know? Sophia had the look of a person refreshed from having worked hard. She would have to rush to catch her plane that evening so she could get back to her practice the next day. We didn't have much time for closing notes or farewells, but would cover what we could. At times we spoke quickly, sharing the news of what we'd experienced, other times we quieted, there were just no words.

"Do you teach what you do?"

"Who's the teacher?"

"What?"

"Who's the teacher?" I tried to let that go. "First, I don't do it. I just happen to be there when it happens. It's a grace."

"Yes, understood."

"I'm only as talented as the person on the table."

"True."

Maybe I'd been too abrupt.

"Once I tried acting. I went for years trying and trying to learn how to act, okay? Well, if you look at actors like Jim Bridges and Kevin Spacey in *K-Pax,* or Julie Harris in *East of Eden,* you catch on that the greatest actors are being what they are. You know? That's the real challenge. And discovering what's in the way. Same with artists. Same with cranial. Some learning of techniques doesn't hurt, but it's not the main thing, same as in acting. So I gave up trying to learn how to act, and worked on just being what I am. Man, did that take me to some interesting places!" I felt a laugh inside my belly. I tried to cut off a smile. "But just being what you are can be quite a small contribution in itself, don't you think?"

"Definitely. What it's all about."

"Well, I don't really know. I've talked to one or two people over the years, but not about techniques really. More about Life. Only one of the people who bothered to show up to the talks was a craniosacral person, or became one after awhile. I guess I'm not all that comfortable with setting myself up as a teacher or making a school of craniosacral or something, I mean, in a formal sense because...it's all teaching. I'm still learning how to just...learn...myself."

"We all are. Do you take insurance?"

"What kind of a question is that now?"

We laughed.

"Seriously? I maybe would, but people with insurance don't really thrive. They don't seem to really want to get better. At least here in this country."

"We do in Canada. No one pays for anything. We all pay for it."

"Yeah, that's wonderful, wonderful. It's a small shift in thinking, right? To tell you the truth, the people I work on from other countries are often in a lot better health than Americans are. It's a mindset. It's like religion here." I looked out at the ocean and its joy. "I don't have health insurance. I don't believe in it. So, I mean, the whole thing about insurance here is that it's a gamble. You pay in money, you make a gamble that you will be sick. You get sick and stay sick, you win! We all know it, on some level, and that's sick!"

We laughed again, almost like we were equals, colleagues.

"How long you been doing this?"

"Awhile, but hardly ever like this. Here at home." I smiled.

"It's working."

"Yeah, I guess I'll get to change my whole way of doing things. Hear of anybody with a place next to the ocean and a swimming pool, let me know okay?"

She smiled. "In New York City? No problem."

"Hawaii? Australia? Oh yeah, it's got to have a theater near-by. With smart actors and actresses!" She had known by now I was also a playwright, the secret was out.

"Why not California? That's kind of where you're based, isn't it?"

"Water's too cold...?"

We both became thoughtful. We'd wanted to go back into the ocean this morning but a wind had come up overnight and the waves rolled in and broke at more than six feet high. It was as if the ocean had pushed us away, said, "No, not now."

"It's amazing what happens when you wait."

"What do you mean?"

"Just like you do. Before going into the ocean. Taking that moment first."

I thought back to the play, the one man show, and how it had taught me to wait before going onstage. I thought how I'd been taking that pause, stopping, taking that moment before, ever since. I didn't feel like admitting to her that I'd discovered it could be done even with the ocean, day before yesterday. The feeling of connection had stayed with us ever since. It was all around us.

"How's your mouth?" I asked.

She touched her cheeks with her fingers and moved her jaw. "Open."

I smiled, "That's good."

Yesterday, in the afternoon session, we worked deep inside the floor of her mouth to give that new harmony in her body even more room to expand. At one point, she felt it appropriate to invite God into the session to watch over her and to support her deeper opening. I felt grateful she did. And it helped to answer why I had been getting so religious on myself in the blend! Then in this morning's session, which we had to perform on the table due to the high surf, my hands started to move all over her body in a flurry of motion being all the techniques at once and opened up spaces in the craniosacral system, in the bodily cavities, internal organs: stomach, pancreas, spleen, intestines. The swirls and spirals had still been moving in their slow motion dance, as if performing their own openings, and although I never mentioned them to her, the feeling that God could be in the room with us during these sessions added a deep feeling of serenity and ease.

She rested on the couches around the house before the afternoon session, and I took an appointment from the area, a friend of a friend who heard I was in town and who had also worked with me in the ocean the day before, the ocean being no less gracious then. This last session with Sophia and I on the table was much calmer and easier, the spirals melted away, and the last of the shadow that had been held in her heart came up out of her mouth, like a concentrated mass of dark gelatin, and with it, the sense of claustrophobia dissolved.

"How 'bout that boat?" I asked.

"Every time I've seen that boat I've felt claustrophobic."

"Really." This was news to me.

"True."

"What was so interesting was just as that...that claustrophobia was going out, the gambling boat turned and went out to sea."

"You said that before," she said. "During the session you mentioned that."

"It was amazing. It was closer in than I'd ever seen it; I thought it was going to crash into the house. It was just going along and right when my hand was at your mouth and taking that gelatinous-mass-thing out..."

"Yes." She breathed.

"It made its turn and headed out."

"So that's where it went, it's on that boat! Good riddance!"

"I meant to show you but...."

"No, it was best." She touched her jaws again. "You realize we couldn't have done the work we did today if we were in the ocean."

"Yes."

The waves weren't so high as they were this morning when she came to the house and the winds had died down in the afternoon. What amazed us was that it all died down suddenly, almost in time for our afternoon session. It was odd. We didn't feel up for it, it didn't feel right, and all we could think to say to the ocean was, "Thank you." And by now, there were steady reports on the kitchen radio of another hurricane off the coasts of the Caribbean called, Frances, already at Category 3. Fierce. Hopefully, it would harmlessly break apart at sea without making landfall.

She had become thoughtful again. "There's some work you can only use a table for."

"True." I lit a cigarette and offered her one.

"No thanks, can't stand the things."

"Some of the best healers I know smoke. Guess they don't believe the propaganda."

"It is propaganda," she agreed. "I just don't like it."

I contemplated the weather and my intuitive weather report. I quietly counted on my fingers. Now, it was late summer of 2004. Victory had been declared in Iraq a little more than one year before, and yet the war had raged on and there seemed to be no end of it. And because of only this, this could make for a lot of stress in the world body. "I hope this next hurricane blows over, but if it doesn't, I can bet it's going to be bad. Just like Charlie was."

"How so?"

"It's the way the Earth throws off stress, same way bodies do. What I mean is...." I stopped myself. I wasn't going to talk about the weather.

"Sure, it always works like that," she said.

"You know this?"

"It makes sense," she said. "After I graduated, I trained with a cranial osteopath in Canada who worked almost exactly the same way we've been working. It's all about consciousness, the weather, all of it."

"Yeah?"

She continued, "Storms are safety valves that release excess energy. It's the same way our bodies work."

"If people were serene and peaceful, we'd have calm skies and oceans."

"I believe that too."

I thought about how weather correspondences had happened before but without our knowing or being alert to them. If I tracked back in history, back before television and the Internet, the great volcano in Indonesia, Krakatoa, erupted after a series of attempted assassinations on key world leaders and right after the surrender of Sitting Bull. Sitting Bull's surrender marked the devastating end of the whole North American Indian culture.

I wanted to say something more, without sounding too unprofessional. "It's elementary, really. Clouds are composed mostly of ions and water, just like our bodies are composed of ions and water. Weather flows with charged electricity, just like our bodies flow with charged electricity. It's the kind of thing we all know, deep down in our bodies, but aren't talking about. Not yet."

We sat in the silence.

"The craniocean effect?" she proposed.

"More like sensitive weather."

We laughed.

"Yeah, and rule number one," I answered, "if ever a major war starts up or an assassination, look to the weather, because that's where it's going to get worked out. Sooner or later, mark my words."

I'd expected her to laugh along but she didn't.

I became aware of the seriousness. Government officials included meteorological studies in their planning and forecasts, but never this, never cataclysmic emotional events on a world scale.

"There's times when weather is just crappy, you know? Once there was a low-grade blow out there and it went on for days. Two people said to me, that same week, it seems the ocean is 'angry'."

"Low grade fever?"

Now, I laughed! "Yeah, anger can do that!"

We fell silent again.

"I wonder about Global Warming," she offered.

"What?" She'd startled me out of my contemplation. "That's almost like saying, what about reincarnation?"

"What do you mean by that?" She became defensive.

I tried to back off. "Well, if there is such a thing...as global warming."

"There is."

"Okay, then, what is global warming?" I answered my own question. "Heating of the earth caused by human activity." I let that sink in for a moment.

"Hah!" She'd laughed out loud.

"Who knows?" I said. "If people had the smallest sense of how we might be connected with the weather, it might still happen but it wouldn't be nearly as intense. And we wouldn't be so intense about it. Instead of freaking out, we might work toward a solution, like, I don't know, energy independence? But we wouldn't have to point fingers, we wouldn't have to act from a place of fear. We wouldn't just be reacting. It would be something that needed to be done, like cleaning dishes or something."

"Exactly," she answered.

The sun glowed bright orange across the beach. It was getting cool out and there was a feeling of ozone in the air, a feeling that often precedes the onslaught of a hurricane.

"It's all in our response," I said.

"Exactly."

I tracked back to Hurricane Gabrielle, a huge tropical storm that could have wrecked havoc on the Southeast. I remembered it well because I was in Freeport, Grand Bahama Island and at work with the dolphins. It had been a bothersome thunderstorm off the southeast coast of Florida, just crappy weather, not worth the mention, but late in the afternoon of September 11th, 2001, it began to accelerate from a non-tropical storm to a tropical cyclone. Chas and Kat and I had watched the news that morning, along with the rest of the world, and when the Hurricane Warnings sounded over the next few days throughout the Bahamas and Florida, I became sick to my stomach. All the country needed now was a hurricane, adding insult to the injury. It increased to hurricane velocity then to everyone's surprise, suddenly decelerated, fell back, and thankfully reduced in velocity to a tropical depression by the time it made landfall on September 14th. Again, I do not mean to discount the very few indirect deaths or the severe flood damage and havoc it caused as it marched northeastwards across the state. Still, it could have been much worse.

But I couldn't understand how it could have decelerated so quickly to a tropical storm, and no one in the Bahamas could either. I'm not a psychotherapist, but in my role as a facilitator, at first the country was in dreadful shock, then in deepest grief, together with the world, and yet all had the capacity to acknowledge and to graciously allow this feeling of grief. It was one event that, like it or not, was freely experienced together. To grieve, appropriately, was all that anyone could do at that time, there was really no other choice. There are many other ways of saying the same thing, but it so happened that this was an appropriate feeling response to disaster, to loss, on a collective scale.

Grief, the old man once pointed out in his soft, plain spoken way, is a feeling. It's not an emotion. He used the analogy of a child getting a skinned knee. If the child keeps picking at the scab, and gets the emotions into it, saying, "Why did this happen", or, "Who's to blame?" the wound can't heal. Best to let the grief pass through. Sometimes there is nothing we can do but just hurt. Once the pain passes, without all the emotions getting into it, we can look around and see what we can do.

After the country had grieved, appropriately, it was able to focus its righteous anger like a lens and to respond appropriately with the world's consent. The Taliban regime collapsed in Afghanistan like a house of cards.

In those few days beginning with September 11th, as Gabriel rapidly accelerated to a tropical cyclone, to a hurricane, and then fell back down, it seemed to me that people were letting their grief pass through them and that they were also in a place, not of anger—everyone seemed too shocked for that—but of gratitude and appreciation for their country and its gifts, and this appreciation was expressed with American flags and the singing of the National Anthem. Also at this time, a memorial service was given at the National Cathedral in Washington which the whole free world watched on television and the President of the United States was at his best. Everyone could let it out. This was far beyond American politics, this was from the soft center of the heart, the place where we are vulnerable and that makes us human. Words of gratitude and appreciation were extended to the families who were suffering and to the Precincts of the brave Fire Fighters and Rescuers who had lost their lives. Hours later, a building Hurricane named Gabrielle would began to decelerate into a Tropical Storm. I watched the very respectful, ritual ceremony on television in a souvenir shop in the Bahamas along with dark skinned Bahamians who were deeply moved as I was. It focused the raw feeling of the tragedy for us and provided a tremendous release for many others around the globe. This was not a reaction, but a response, and as a response, a noble acknowledgment and acceptance of pain and true grief. It passed like the storm.

I thought of the word, 'thank you.'

When I myself had suffered a stomach ache or a backache, for example, I learned to see the symptom as a normal adaptation to stress and the byproducts of stress, and even to say, 'thank you.' The more I would say this, the better I would feel. It wouldn't make the backache go away all at once, but the adaptation would become a learning process and the healing would become activated. I could accept the physical discomfort and find what I could do about it, if anything. And I'd feel better on the instant, whatever the adaptation was doing. How many times had I ever attempted to say a simple, 'thank you,' to an adaptation the Earth was evidently going through? Was this possible for anyone to do? And, like Ada Lopez in Puerto Rico, when a major storm threatened, how many times had I ever dared "blend with the wind?" Not that this meant I had to go out to the beach or anything during a storm! I could say 'thank you' anywhere, even during the weather reports on television!

"Okay, so I'm the guy who says if they really want change in the world, even in the Middle East, instead of start more wars and drop more bombs and pollute the places out of all recognition, airlift in thousands of craniosacral therapists, acupuncturists, massage therapists, even energy workers, set up heavily guarded clinics and go to work on the people."

She nodded. "An awful lot of trauma there."

"Yeah, but instead of release bombs, release the emotions that throw the bombs! That is, if you really want change."

"That would work. That would actually work."

"It would create lasting change on all sides. That is, if we really wanted change."

"Yes."

"And turn the other cheek."

"Turn the other...?"

I moved my head one way and then another. "Different point of view? Watch the cheek?"

She was serious once more. "Yes."

Wherever you are, there YOU are.

I could feel a smile well up inside. How could I explain this to Dad? Finally, I had someone I could speak to this about! Even the great Osteopath knew about the weather and human emotions! But we didn't have the time.

"Can I say something? A technical question?"

"Try me."

Suddenly, I felt I was onstage. And a little uncomfortable sharing something in words with her that I didn't fully understand myself. But what was the point if there was no thinking outside the box, no questioning, no learning? Learning is always mutual or there's no learning at all. "Okay, Dr. Upledger says the craniosacral system is the system where the body, mind, and spirit integrate, okay? It's where they all come together, you know? Where they come together and influence all the other physiological systems in the body, okay? But I look at the space around us, at the environment, I look at the work we've been doing in the ocean, and it's all living and...participating. It's not as if this space all around us...is inert."

"True."

I felt a wave of enthusiasm pass through. "What if the craniosacral system isn't just the place where the body, mind, and spirit come together, but the place where the living environment comes together too? So it's not just body, mind, and spirit, but it's....." I counted on my fingers, unlike me. "Body, mind, spirit, and living environment? All in an interface!"

"Sure, of course, living," she said. "Everything's interconnected. It's all consciousness." She made it seem so simple. It's all interconnected. And it is all alive with consciousness. This is the benefit of experience. I wanted to express my admiration of her. "But Sutherland's pointed this out all along. And he got it from Still."

"Has he?" I asked.

She paused. "Look, you've got this thing about Upledger. I had a thing going on about Sutherland. I had to get over it. They're old guys with techniques, that's all, and it's all to be transcended...if you're to grow. But you know all this already. Why are you asking me anything?"

Maybe she didn't quite understand what I'd said. But yes, there were other teachers besides those two, other schools of craniosacral, other techniques. And all to be transcended. She had astonished me.

"How long you been at this game?"

"Too long."

I laughed and coughed through the laugh. She gave me a look, as if to say, smokers' cough? I stubbed my cigarette out in an empty planter, looked at my notes. Her taxi was on the way to take her to the airport and we only had a few more minutes. "Feedback on our last session?"

"The one just now?" She shifted in her chair and looked out

at the ocean. "I like the pool. It's more...contained."

"Yes, it is."

"Not so many waves."

I noted this down, checked my other notes. So we'd started our last session on the massage table but ended in the pool. It was a general calming with some easy unwinds and wide stretches off the edge of the table and after awhile, she began to make delicate motions with her hands and fingers as if they were helping her to open more. And with this motion, I realized I had no difficulty remembering her name. Sophia, I'd say to myself. Sophia is your name. I wouldn't tell her this, of course, and when we got into the pool and its heated water, her body welcomed the warmth and again she stretched and with her eyes closed, she began to make the same quiet motions with her hands, brushing her fingers delicately over her ribs to her shoulders and beyond. It made sense to be here in the pool, if only for more of a general calming and integration of the work we'd done in the past few days. There had been a great weight on her upper chest, around her heart, and now she was letting her hands free her. As she floated, I happened to look around the sides of the pool and standing with us, at discrete intervals—it's impossible to describe this—were fantastically bright angels and there was a sense of song. It wasn't like a crowd, just a few around the corners and sides of the pool deck. I wondered if I should clear out of the pool and run. But I stood my ground and allowed this too. I didn't mention anything about them aloud, for such information could alarm her and what's worse, interfere with her very personal process. To mention them would have been plain, bad manners, after all, she might see something entirely different, or like Ada Lopez, just sense the feeling of care and comfort without seeing anything at all. This was my own subjective world, I guessed, and I made myself as comfortable as I could. But I couldn't help remember she'd invited God into the sessions before this and I asked her now. "Would it be okay to invite God in?"

"Yes", she said. "I already have."

All I could find words for was, "Thank you." It was as if the angels were with us in all that we had done. The sun was an hour or so from setting and I took in the blueness of the sky. I felt grateful that the ocean wouldn't let us in this morning. If we would have worked in the ocean how much we would have missed. She continued to float, occasionally making the delicate motions of opening with her wrists and fingers. She didn't go out to the deep end of the pool but only once. The wind had picked up in the higher altitudes but not that much on the ground and the pool had hardly a ripple. We mostly stayed around the shallows and I was able to maintain gentle contact without doing much of anything. I began to enjoy the feeling of ease and I wasn't so disturbed by the angels being there now and I thought of my many teachers, all the way back to the First Baptist Church of West Palm Beach, and it was that simple feeling of being in gratitude. "I feel my whole body can breathe," she said. It took me a moment to answer, "Wonderful."

I'd heard these words before from clients in L.A. and I vaguely recalled a term of Dr. Sutherland's, Breath of Life. It didn't seem that anyone understood it so I'd forgotten about it. It came back to me now. I felt a wash of happiness for her and smiled and floated with her and looked at the eves of the partial red tile roof above the Florida room that opened out to the sun deck and sky, and looked again. Far above the pool was a small cloud form, almost perfect for the size of the pool. I thought of the clouds that had surrounded Kat, but it wasn't anything like a storm cloud. The cloud had taken on the same shape that Sophia had been tracing over her chest with her hands, as if the sky were a living reflection of her opening. And the cloud arose in a thin, gossamer column from the south and then bifurcated to spread out into two branches overhead, the opening from the center of her chest. Sophia kept moving her hands and fingers delicately over her chest and letting them spread out behind her in the water. Who could I tell? Who would believe me? I realized I wasn't about that. I was about others' finding out for themselves and making their own discoveries. "Sophia," I whispered, not wanting to disturb her. But this was too good for her to miss. "Look up." "What?" She opened her eyes. I pointed to the sky. She wiped the water out of the corners of her eyes. The cloud pattern remained directly over the pool, despite the growing late afternoon winds, and she began to laugh! The laughter filled her body, mind, and spirit with a sound of human Being. And now, with my inner seeing: above her forehead shone a luminous, little blue flower. The covering shadow that had been there when we first met was no longer there. Sophia was back. She had found her way. She kept her eyes open and settled back into the water, a soft smile on her lips. It was a prayer and without words, a prayer of water and sky and of being alive. It was truly delightful for both of us to experience.

"How about that cloud?"

"Yes." She looked up into the sky. "That was amazing!"

The cloud was long gone now. It had been over us only while we were in the pool. "Truly amazing."

She reflected. "I wonder if it happens all the time and we don't notice."

A few months later, I would talk with her on the phone and tell her I'd seen this same event occur with the clouds above the office in Los Angeles. Although it didn't happen all the time, clouds had a tendency to mirror the results of sessions when the work was deeply focused and concentrated. I shared this event with Sophia more to comfort her. For example, the clouds above Melrose had mirrored an ovarian problem with a middle-aged woman who'd flown in from out-of-state for a session. We found that her left ovary was much too full of fluid and needed to re-lax so it could safely drain and balance with her other ovary. By the end, she said she could actually feel the size of her left ovary decrease and balance with her right ovary. Since hers was the last session of the day, I'd stepped out and just happened to look up and there was one wispy cloud in the "U" shape of a uterus with two smaller cloud-shaped-ovaries attached to either side. There was also a thin bluish stripe of a cloud leading out of one of the cloud ovaries on one side which to me was the mirror image of the needed drainage. The cloud pattern remained like this for twenty minutes or more before it broke apart. Keep in mind there doesn't need to be an "emotional release" session for this to occur in the firmament, only focused work, a sense of connection, and that this is possible.

Both Sophia and I had heard of stories and legends about Buddhist Lamas, gurus, and shamans who could make rain or even stop tornadoes, but I feel this kind of event doesn't occur on personal command or by force or with clock-like regularity. It does seem to occur if we are merely open to it occurring and if we can include the living environment, ocean, water, clouds, sky, sunlight, within our loving intention to heal, or, be healed.

By then, I'd heard of similar events occurring with other cran-iosacral practitioners—on the Gulf Coast and in Hawaii—but only when the work was deeply focused and concentrated. This tells me that this is not unique to CraniOcean work. The ocean can respond to us the way we see her and respond. When I share these stories with other practitioners, who are open to it, both they and their clients begin to see and experience it too. It is for them to tell their own stories someday.

Don't get me wrong. I don't go running outside each professional day to see if the results of focused sessions are reflected in the clouds above! I'll be the first to point out that this is not beyond humor. Humor is essential. Laughter is, after all, the best medicine!

If you're not a practitioner, and would at least like to get a sense on your own of what it is to float, you could start to play with something as simple as a soft, flexible foam Water Noodle or *Fun Noodle* from a Dollar Store. It could be of any color, red, green, blue, purple, clear. Place one long Noodle under the back of your head, at the occiput, and one under your knees, or ankles, and allow yourself to just float. You might invite a friend to join you and take turns. Call it, conscious rest. See what happens!* It can be performed in any body of water, even a lake or stream in the mountains. Yes, this can be experienced in the mountains. In fact, it was from walking in the woods in New England in my teens that I felt the first impulse and feeling of walking with nature and blending with it. When we take a moment to sit or stand quietly and with attention in the woods, *something happens.* There is an invitation to each of us to open and to blend with the trees, water, sunlight, and all we need do is graciously accept and say, Yes. It is always there for us. If you do this, the worst that can happen is you'd both become so deeply relaxed in the quiet corner of a pool, or in the waters of the ocean, that you wouldn't care about what the weather is doing! And that's okay too. There's really nothing to force. Just enjoy! I often suggest floating like this as a relaxing self-treatment in CraniOcean. This may truly be what *noodling* is about!

* *The Reader is invited to check out a proposed website in the References section at the end of this book where anyone of any background might share similar stories and experiences about Sensitive Weather, using the World Wide Web.*

Then she said, "There's something I'd like to say."

I hoped she'd go easy on me. My fears were for naught. She opened up more and told me some of what she had been experiencing after the morning session that day while she rested at the house. She had had a boyfriend that she'd mentioned once or twice outside of sessions but I didn't give it much thought or pursue the matter. This fellow had been verbally and physically abusive to her during their relationship, much like her dad had been abusive to her as a child, and she had doubts of ever having a successful relationship in the future. She'd said that when she first met this guy, her whole body tightened up and ever since then, she'd always suffered from constipation and would overeat. Also, that she had planned to meet another man in the City the next day, a man whom she'd felt was a really decent man, and this accounted for her rush to depart. This reminded me her taxi was on the way and we'd been talking for a full twenty minutes. She continued. This new man was a man she felt she could trust. Also, after the first session that morning, she realized she wasn't thinking about her ex-boyfriend, she wasn't "obsessing" on him like she had almost every day since he broke up with her seven years ago. "It's all in the body," I said. "Yes," she agreed. She had tried to get in touch with him over the years but he would refuse to return her calls or make any effort to get back in touch with her, and each time he did this, she felt unworthy and not good enough for anyone. "I was so filled up with him I couldn't breathe!" She touched her chest, breathed, and did the same motion of opening with her hands that was reflected like a living mirror in the cloud pattern.

I listened through the rush of story coming out of her body and I thought, "Man, why save it all back for later?" I consoled myself that she'd been inwardly aware of her process as it was occurring, even when in silence, and that dialogue wasn't necessary for her. It dawned on me that the silent work, the subtle work, is no less profound, provided there is an openness to being aware of all that is going on within and all that is going on without, moment by moment. She would pick the session up again with her psychological counselor later on and this was the way it worked best for her.

I let it go.

A few months later in that same follow up phone conversation, she would tell me she'd had lunch with her colleagues in the City and had mentioned her new relationship to them and said if it weren't for the work in the ocean, she never would've been able to enjoy it. Her colleagues agreed that the work in the ocean helped her through her new relationship. It wasn't easy, of course, but it was nothing like what she'd experienced in her past. I asked her how she liked the ocean work? She said that before the ocean work it was hard to let go. And that it was hard for her patients to let go. They didn't see the support they had all around them. Nor did she. She was able to let go of the pain due to the support of the environment, able to let go of the heaviness so more space opened to be lighter. "Sometimes," she said, "you need all the support and to be around that ocean, that sky...there's always so much here to support us and we don't even know. We're always in our little rooms in the city and we don't look up, we don't see it."

I thought what she said was beautiful. And I asked her to e-mail it to me in her own words, if she could put it into words, for a book I was planning about the ocean, the weather, the house.

"Why a book?" she asked.

"Well, to show what we were talking about, to show what's possible. I mean, you're a doctor..."

"I'm not a Doctor."

She's not? "But isn't an osteopath a doctor?"

"Not in Canada, not necessarily." She laughed. "Did you think I was a doctor?"

Dad thought an Osteopath was a doctor too.

"No," I said. "I mean, yes. You're a healer."

She was very precise. "I finished my studies in Osteopathy at the College of Osteopathy of Montreal with a diploma. My course of study followed the traditional osteopathic teaching from Sutherland and Still. That simple."

"Oh." I didn't know what to say. "Well, I get accused of being a Doctor myself sometimes!"

She laughed. "I'll send you your letter for your book."

I was quick to say, "It's not *my* book."

"Then who's book is it?"

"I don't know. Life, the Universe, the Cosmos? I didn't write it. Life did."

"Whatever, James!"

IN SOPHIA'S OWN WORDS

Working as a practitioner of cranial osteopathy, I realize that if we can feel the incredibly loving support from the environment from inside our clinics and offices, our patients will also feel that love, and let go of their controls and allow themselves to express, let go, and heal.

Opening to this has helped me be comfortable with myself and has allowed me to be thoughtful and compassionate toward others. When there is anger and stress of course the root is some pain or fear that lingers in the tissues.

More personally, I released the pain in the CraniOcean sessions and releasing old pain, purely feeling it and letting it go strengthens you and allows you to cope with sensitive issues that inevitably, come up in relationships. If we carry the wounds of our child, those wounds stop us from feeling: we rather numb ourselves than actually allow ourselves to feel. There is so much pain underneath we are blocked from feeling new emotions, painful or joyful.

Being treated in the ocean, outdoors with full view of the sky, allowed me to see the support I was receiving and that helped me to release the pain. I realized that is why it is hard for some of my patients to let go, they don't see the support of the environment while being treated in our offices.

I have done extensive healing work in the past 10 years. What was offered me with the CraniOcean treatments was very different from past experiences because I felt the enormous support of the ocean and sky during the treatments. The loving support of the environment is not only possible, it helped me to let go of the heaviness so more space is open to be filled with new emotions, cleaner thoughts and feelings from head to uterus. And the pain that was released from my ears from abuse as a kid, I felt as though the memory was inside of me, and the ocean lifted it and supported me in such a way that I was capable of remembering the pain safely, and to cope with the feelings the memories held. Feeling the pain of the memory allowed me to totally release it out of my tissues, being left completely free of the trauma. Sometimes you need all the support around you, and to be around that ocean and that sky and those clouds, we don't even know how much love there is from the universe. We're always in our little rooms and we don't look up, we don't see it while we are indoors. The environment provides that loving support, we just need to be aware of it to use it to its fullest capacity.

The ocean's water allowed me to float, James was working and when I gave my trust to the ocean, my body unraveled itself with her and I was able to express the sadness and fear that I unknowingly have been holding onto since childhood.

I feel that the loving support of the environment was the needed force that allowed my subconscious to feel safe enough to let go. All of a sudden, I could let go of my control, because I felt supported by something far greater than any one person.

—Sophia Karras D.O.M.P. (Quebec)

The weather was clear for her departure. Hurricane Frances wouldn't make landfall for another four days, and I had to pack for my own flight to L.A. to work with the married couple from Santa Barbara. As it turned out, I was on one of the last planes out before the airport was shut down. I could feel the winds of the storm rattle the back of the plane, pushing it west. I wished I could have stayed longer to help secure the house. I would hear of Frances in Los Angeles and see the front page photograph in the *L.A. Times* of three sailboats slung up like palm trees against the low granite pilings at Singer Island. Then all too soon would follow the strongest, Ivan the Terrible. Both would make landfall at Sewel's Point, about forty miles north in Stuart, both would do massive damage with loss of human life.

This book was written in the Fall of 2004. I would put these catastrophic events together with the shock of the invasion of Iraq in 2003, given the necessary lag time. I couldn't know of the massive hurricanes that would occur the next year, notably Katrina, likely following the world reaction to the shock of the Abu Ghraib prison tortures on the part of the United States, or, of the Tsunami that would wreak havoc in Indonesia and beyond, likely following the shock of the 2002 terrorist bombing in Bali. As other tragic world events continue to unfold with terrible suddenness, I could only expect that more catastrophic meteorological disasters would occur around our beautiful earth, without

knowing exactly when. And well, so what? If such events do occur or do not, might the real challenge be to observe our own reactions? And in observing, stop the reaction?

In stopping the reaction, response can occur, the infinitely
creative response of Spirit.

I waved to Sophia from the deck as she got into the yellow
cab down in the driveway. She was in a hurry, but happy. I
watched as the taxi pulled out, turned up the hill, and rounded
the curve to head south on the ocean road toward the bridges that
connected Palm Beach to West Palm Beach and the airport. It was
getting chilly. I went back through Dad's bathroom to the hall
and downstairs to the Florida room and looked at the massage
table. The room was quiet and still. I never knew that the house
could serve as a place of healing, not the house I grew up in. But
the house had always served as a place of healing for our family,
friends, and for others too, I'd just never noticed. Maybe all houses were like this, or could be, if we could only see them this way
and give them the chance. I took in the emptiness of the room.
I wandered into the parlor, the blue room. I looked at the silver
framed photograph of my mom and dad on the piano, the photograph from their 50th wedding anniversary. She looked so beautiful in her sparkling gown as she walked down the aisle of the
chapel, radiant, like an angel. And Dad in his fine tuxedo with
tails, so vital, proud, and happy. I felt grateful that I'd had the privilege to be their son. My head bowed and I thanked them and
my hands made that same motion of clouds. I spoke to the photograph, "Well, there's more than one way to join the Navy!"

EPILOGUE

Why not end here with a tribute to John Lilly, MD, the granddaddy of all dolphin researchers, famous for his legendary research on LSD, altered states, extraterrestrial life forms, and the creation of the Floatation Tank, featured in the 1980's movie with William Hurt, *Altered States*?

This is off the beaten path but it happened, make of it what you will. My journal says this happened on September 10, 2001. When I was taking my first course in the Bahamas and just learning the art of swimming with the dolphins, we were at the end of the day and hanging out on the top deck of the Institute research vessel, the *Dolphin Star,* and this guy came up to us from the docks with his girlfriend and started talking and he somehow knew all about craniosacral, its history, Sutherland, the dates, all of it, and this amazed us. Later on, he wandered back alone on the docks in his swimming trunks on his way to the gift shop, and I was alone and I called down to him and invited up to the top deck of the *Dolphin Star,* for a sample craniosacral session. And he was up for it, he was cool, and he said he had never had any massage or bodywork or chiropractic in his life. This would be the first time he'd let anyone, you know, touch him this way.

He was middle-aged, a bit taller than me, and strong and he was fit, and his girlfriend had mentioned he was quite a healer himself. She said he could just lay on his hands and you'd feel better instantly. He did it with everyone. And he made his living as an entrepreneur in South Florida. So he was up for it, and said his back and shoulders were sore because he and his girlfriend had just driven over on his Rybovitch Outboard in very rough waters from Florida. So he got on the table in his bathing suit, and I arced him, and it was as if he had another body inside of his body. And there was texture to this other body, a definite, very smooth texture, in a shade of very dark green, while on the outside, he looked just like a regular guy. And on some level, he knew that I knew. And I would have called someone else on the vessel to arc him along with me, but I sensed it would have been invasive to him. I felt grateful that no one had ever told me something like this couldn't happen. So I continued to work with him for twenty minutes or so and was astonished at how quickly and easily he corrected: the problem was that both of his bodies needed to readjust into a kind of fit and alignment with each other. His fleshy body felt almost like a rubbery shell and yet his true body was much darker with the texture of a smooth, almost vascular skin. It was interesting to me but for the moment, I tried to let it go. I found him to be quite pleasant, and we both knew just when he'd achieved the fit he'd needed, which did happen to occur with a deep core alignment. It was only at the end of the session that I let myself experience the wonder of it, this man of an unknown alien species in a human form. My hands eased off, I backed away from the table. He thanked me, got off the research vessel, and went off in his swimsuit to the gift shop or somewhere. I never saw him again, and I was sorry about that because I liked him. He was really a very nice guy and well mannered. I guessed it's what was possible, all that could happen on this day job.

None of what I had experienced with him was scientifically verifiable. There were no objective studies made, no hard data sheets, and no Double Blind studies. And my notions of the weather? If I was to be true to myself, not false, I would as well have spent the time looking for the Hidden Meaning of License Plates. Was it just for the fun of it then?

I looked at the sunlight through the bright clouds. There was a silence in the air. All I was left with was a simple feeling of being in gratitude. This was to last.

END

ACKNOWLEDGMENTS

I thank the unsung process of heroes and heroines who have graciously and generously permitted their stories be put to paper and contributed to others they may never know or meet.

I thank those who have permitted their actual names to be used in this book and their session stories to be told.

I thank my family for allowing me to share experiences that I had with my dad in the house we all grew up in. I thank my six sisters, my dad and my mom.

I often see myself as setting up plays for the stage in each new clinic where I work. I thank Dr. John E. Upledger for encouraging student writings which would appeal to those less medically orientated to the field. In 2002, on Dr. Upledger's birthday, I mentioned to him that I was planning such a book and I thank him for very generously giving me the permission to use terms from Upledger Craniosacral Therapy, and for his admonition to make the book my own. I'm glad for this challenge for it helped to inspire these words to be put on the page in the early stages and to complete this book, a book which would turn into a series of books, and for this I'm also grateful.

I thank Dr. Andrew Still for his inspiration and continuing influence over the field in all its facets. I thank William Sutherland, DO, for first discovering this healing art. I appreciate John E. Upledger, DO, for picking up the ball where Dr. Sutherland left off and simplifying and expanding this healing art so folks like me could get it and what's more, make it our own. I thank

Arnold Mindell, creator of Process Work®, the Cranial Academy, visionary Artist, kaleidoscopic philosopher, Roger Weir, J. Krishnamurti of Ojai and the *Krishnamurti Foundation,* Dr. Robert Rhondell Gibson, "Dr. Bob," creator of both The Picture of Man and *The Science of Man: 48 Lessons,* and the many other doctors, scientists and educators who's pioneering research contributed to the synthesis that would become CraniOcean. I also thank my colleagues at the Upledger Institute, and my first teachers there who encouraged me to go forward, Avadan Larson, Suzanne Schurlock Durana, and Chas Perry, Ph.D, and of those who permitted their names to be mentioned in this book, including Alice Quaid.

I thank those who have trained with me, and I thank those who have trusted me to work with them in this healing art. I thank those who allowed their stories to be written in this book and in other books I've written.

I thank the good hearted massage therapists and intuitive body workers and healers—energy workers of all the schools I have encountered, not just of the Upledger Institute, and acknowledge them all as one of the greatest natural human resources on the planet at this time. I have learned something from each one that I have had the privilege to encounter, touch, or be touched by, teach, or be taught by, on both coasts, and deeply acknowledge their silent contribution to this book, from the wings.

Our greatest natural human resource?

For one example, rather than drop bombs, nations may discover that CranioSacral Therapists, Massage Therapists, and Energy Workers can be airlifted into hot spots around the world, with special preparations made by the military to secure clinics in which they would work to heal the area, from the inside-out!

I thank each friend and colleague who read and commented or made notes on this book, especially since I hadn't a clue how to tackle this outside the Nonfiction form, and those, including my sisters, who patiently listened to me read parts of it out loud. I thank a dear friend, Merilee Eliot, who read the core draft, written in two weeks, and who encouraged me to go forward. Also, Editorial Consultant, Lisa Marguerite Mora, Bill Groetzinger, layout design, and George Foster for a delightful cover.

I thank all of my teachers not just in healing art, but also in theater art, including the great, Ms. Julie Harris, who faithfully stuck it out with me all these years and provided a stellar example of what it is to be a human being. I thank Charles Nelson Reilly, Burt Reynolds, and my good friend and support in Los Angeles, Veteran actor, Louis Turrene. I also thank another friend, Rysard Cieslak of the Polish Laboratory Theater, who first pointed me to the Transformational possibilities of Theater.

I also thank Mr. Phil Blecker, who first introduced "Rhondell's" information to me in informal talks at his place in Glendale, California, and for taking the time with me on the phone. I thank Chiropractor, Dr. Robert Galas, who trusted the process enough to allow me the time to work with his patients in the Back Room, a marvelous laboratory. Also, Joe Bankhead, for his humor and wisdom as a "Sillyosopher".

I thank my teachers, known and unknown, seen and unseen, past, present, and future. Love and thanks to all who contributed to this book.

Thank you each and all for the share of your consciousness with ours here in the blend. I wish for you each wonderful experiences of every color, tone and magnitude. If these words have served to give you a smile on your way, or be of good use to someone we may never know or meet, its job will be done.

REFERENCES

SOFT SYSTEMS

1 Soft Systems Methodology (SSM) is an approach to organizational process modeling developed in England by Peter Checkland, Brian Wilson and others, and used here intuitively. The Author has long used only the phrase, "Soft Systems" to describe human biological systems, and the craniosacral system in particular. There is no direct association.

MY LIFE GOES OFF TRACK

1 *The Essential Rumi,* translated by Coleman Barks with John Moyne, Harper San Francisco, 1995, pg. 270. Reprinted here with the generous permission of Coleman Barks.

THE THIRD

1 *The Waste Land, V. What the Thunder Said,* T.S.Eliot, *T. S. Eliot, The Complete Poems and Plays, 1909-1950,* Harcourt, Brace, and World, Inc., New York, 1971, stanza 360-366, pg. 48

THE COLOR BLUE

1 Paraphrase based on, *Commentaries on Living, First Series,* J. Krishnamurti, 1989, Theosophical Publishing House, Wheaton, IL, USA, p. 205

One passage reads, "The movement of becoming, of the man who wants to be the Buddha or the manager, is the activity of the shallow. The shallow are ever afraid of what they are; but what they are is the truth."

2 From the *Brihadaranyaka Upanishad,* 1.3.28

3 Paraphrase based on, *Autobiography of a Yogi,* Paramahansa Yogananda, Self Realization Fellowship Publishers, Los Angeles, CA, Chapter 30

VERY SENSITIVE CHAOS

1 *Sensitive Chaos: The Creation of Flowing Forms in Water and Air,* Theodor Schwenk, revised translation by J.Collis, Preface by Jacques Cousteau, Rudolf Steiner Press, London, revised translation, 1996

TRINIDAD AND TOBAGO

1 There are numerous sites and article on this subject, including, *Ancient Walking Whales Shed Light on Ancestry of Ocean Giants,* National

Geographic News, David Braun, September 19, 2001, *http://news.nationalgeographic.com/news/2001/09/0919_walkingwhale.html*

2 There are also numerous sites and articles on this, including, *Whale Ancestors: Origins Research, The Thewisson Lab,* sourced with ease on Google.

3 *The Essential Rumi,* translated by Coleman Barks with John Moyne, Harper San Francisco, 1995, pg. 137. Reprinted by permission of Coleman Barks.

EMOTIONAL WEATHER PATTERNS

1 The Reader might refer to, *A Stormy Star,* by Curt Suplee, and *Special Supplement: The Sun,* National Geographic.com/Magazine, July, 2004.

The "I DON'T KNOW SHELF"

1 The phrase, *THE I DON'T KNOW SHELF,* is used here by permission of the Catalog of Rhondell Material. The phrase is the, "Old Man's." Refer to the small press book, *Who's In Charge of My Inner State of Being?,* and, *Original Headlines, Science of Man,* by Rhondell, Published by Rhondell Publishing Company, 1993. *http://www.rhondell.com/*

2 Written by Ted Perry, inspired by a speech by Chief Seattle. Reprinted here with the generous permission of Ted Perry.

"NO TECHNIQUES"

1 This beautiful passage is taken from the King James Version, Job 12:7-10

2 *The Gift: Poems by Hafiz, The Great Sufi Master,* translated by Daniel Landinsky, Penguin Compass, Published by Penguin Group, 1999, pg. 159.

CLOSING NOTES AND FAREWELLS

1 The reader is invited to check out a *proposed* website for anyone to share similar stories about Sensitive Weather, using the World Wide Web. Stories can be as random as the sun coming out during a marriage proposal, or rain during a memorial service. To share your stories, just for fun, go to the professional trade website, *http://www.CraniOcean.com.* Don't forget to bring your sense of humor!

CraniOcean Media
CraniOcean.com

QUICK ORDER FORM

Fax Orders: **(801) 785-0188.** *Send this form.*

Phone Orders: **(866) 669-3627.** *Toll Free, arranged by RazorPages*

Email Orders: **Info@RazorPages.com** *Specify book title, quantity and contact information*

Postal Orders: **Razorpages — Orders, 2989 South 300 W. Salt Lake City, Utah 84115**

Yes, I'd like to receive: *TOUCH THE OCEAN: The Power Of Our Collective Emotions.* I understand that I may return this book for a full refund — for any reason, no questions asked.

Name _____

Address _____

City _____ State _____ Zip _____

Email _____

Also, please send *TOUCH THE OCEAN:*
To: *The Power Of Our Collective Emotions*

Name _____

Address _____

City _____ State _____ Zip _____

Email _____

Sales Tax: Please add 7.75% for shipping to California addresses.
Shipping by air: *U.S.:* $4.00 for first book and $2.00 for each additional.
International: $9.00 for first book, $5.00 for each additional (estimate)

CRANIOCEAN MEDIA'S
FORTHCOMING BOOKS:

JOURNEYS:
STORIES OUR BODIES CAN TELL

Actual Case Histories from the deeper levels
of CranioSacral Therapy, where it doesn't matter
what the modality or approach is called!

AWAKE AND ASLEEP:
STORIES OUR BODIES CAN TELL

The third book in this series. An enlightening
exploration of the human body's possibilities.

THE HIDDEN MEANING OF LICENSE PLATES:
A MEMOIR OF SPIRITUAL
SELF IMPROVEMENT

A total and delightful surprise!

Make sure to visit *CraniOcean.com* for more!

Register any email address on *CraniOcean.com*
for key information!

Advanced Orders through *RazorPages.*
See our QUICK ORDER FORM for more!

Thank you.

CAN ONE LIGHT TOUCH CHANGE THE WORLD?

The standard amount of touch pressure used in Craniosacral Therapy is about 5 grams, or the weight of a nickel. Place a nickel on the back of your hand and you'll discover how light a touch can be. Go ahead and find a nickel. Find out for yourself!

Here's something else you can find out for yourself. This simple exercise can be done by anyone at home or even in public.

I was in a West Palm Beach grocery store check-out line. I was in a hurry and needed to get the attention of a young Hispanic man in front of me. He was engaged in a passionate conversation with his spouse. I tapped on his arm. No response. Tapped again. Nothing. Then I thought to touch his arm very lightly. He sprang backwards to look at me! The next time you would like someone's attention, even if you don't know them, simply touch them with the most minimal pressure (with the weight of a nickel), and see what happens. If you do this with care and correctly, you'll be surprised. Now, I am easily able to maneuver through crowded restaurants and packed bars — all it takes is a very light touch!

What could this mean for you in your World?